Student Note-Taking Guide to accompany

Drugs
and
Society

Eighth Edition

Glen R. Hanson

Peter J. Venturelli

Annette E. Fleckenstein

JONES AND BARTLETT PUBLISHERS

Sudbury, Massachusetts

BOSTON   TORONTO   LONDON   SINGAPORE

World Headquarters
Jones and Bartlett Publishers
40 Tall Pine Drive
Sudbury, MA 01776
978-443-5000
info@jbpub.com
www.jbpub.com

Jones and Bartlett Publishers Canada
2406 Nikanna Road
Mississauga, ON L5C 2W6
CANADA

Jones and Bartlett Publishers International
Barb House, Barb Mews
London W6 7PA
UK

Cover Images: (top) © AbleStock and PhotoDisc; (bottom) Frederic Cirou/PhotoAlto/Picture Quest

Printed in the United States of America
08 07 06 05 04   10 9 8 7 6 5 4 3 2 1

Contents

How This Book Can Help You Learn

All of us have different learning styles. Some of us are visual learners, some auditory, some learn better by doing an activity. Some students prefer to learn new material using visual aids. Some learn material better when they hear it in a lecture; others learn it better by reading it. Cognitive research shows that no matter what your learning style, you will learn more if you are actively engaged in the learning process.

The *Student Note-Taking Guide* will help you learn by providing a structure to your notes and letting you utilize all of the learning techniques mentioned above. Students don't need to copy every word their professor says or recopy their entire textbook. Do the assigned reading, listen in lecture, follow the key points your instructor makes, and write down meaningful notes. After reading the text and listening to lectures, review your notes and pull out the most important points.

This *Guide* is a great learning tool that follows the chapter topics presented in your textbook, *Drugs and Society, Eighth Edition.* If your instructor is using the PowerPoint slides that accompany the text, this guide will save you from having to write down everything that is on the slides. There is space provided for you to jot down the terms and concepts that you feel are most important to each lecture. By working with this guide, you are seeing, hearing, writing, and, later, reading and reviewing. The more often you are exposed to the material, the better you will learn and understand it. Using different methods of exposure significantly increases your comprehension.

This is the perfect place to write down questions that you want to ask your professor later, interesting ideas that you want to discuss with your study group, or reminders to yourself to go back and study a particular concept again to make sure that you really got it.

Having organized notes is essential when studying for an exam, or when doing homework assignments. Your ability to easily locate the important concepts of a recent lecture will help you move along more rapidly, as you don't have to spend time rereading an entire chapter just to reinforce one point that you may not have completely understood.

This *Guide* is a valuable resource. You've found a wonderful study partner!

Note-Taking Tips

1. It is easier to take notes if you are not hearing the information for the first time. Read the chapter or the material that is about to be discussed before class. This will help you to anticipate what will be said in class and have an idea of what to write down. It will also help to read over your notes from the previous class. This way you can avoid having to spend the first few minutes of class trying to remember where you left off last time.

2. Don't waste your time trying to write down everything that your professor says. Instead, listen closely and write down only the important points. Review these points after class to remind you of related points that were made during the lecture.

3. If the class discussion takes a spontaneous turn, pay attention and participate in the discussion. Only take notes on the conclusions that are relevant to the lecture.

4. Emphasize main points in your notes. You may want to use a highlighter, special notation (asterisks, exclamation points), format (circle, underline), or placement on the page (indented, bulleted). You will find that when you try to recall these points, you will be able to actually picture them on the page.

5. Be sure to copy specific formulas, laws, and theories word-for-word.

6. Hearing something repeated, stressed, or summed up can be a signal that it is an important concept to understand.

7. Organize handouts, study guides, and exams in your notebook along with your lecture notes. It may be helpful to use a three-ring binder, so that you can insert pages wherever you need to.

8. When taking notes, you might find it helpful to leave a wide margin on all four sides of the page. Doing this allows you to note names, dates, definitions, etc. for easy access and studying later. It may also be helpful to make notes of questions you want to ask your professor about or research later, ideas or relationships that you may want to explore more on your own, or concepts that you don't fully understand.

9. It is best to maintain a separate notebook for each class. Labeling and dating your notes can be helpful when you need to look up information from previous lectures.

10. Make your notes legible, and take notes directly in your notebook. Chances are you won't recopy them no matter how noble your intentions. Spend the time you would have spent recopying the notes studying them instead, drawing conclusions and making connections that you didn't have time for in class.

11. Look over your notes after class while the lecture is still fresh in your mind. Fix illegible items and clarify anything you don't understand. Do this again right before the next class.

Chapter 1: Introduction to Drugs and Society

Notes

Drug Use

- Drug users are found in all occupations and professions, at all income and social class levels, and in all age groups.
- No one is immune to drug use, which often leads to drug dependence. Thus, drug use is an *equal-opportunity affliction.*

Four Principal Factors That Affect Drug Use

- **Pharmacological**: How a particular drug affects the body.
- **Cultural Factors**: How society's views are determined by custom and tradition.
- **Social Factors**: Include specific reasons why a drug is taken, such as peer group members, family upbringing, membership in subcultures, etc.
- **Contextual Factors**: The physical surroundings where the drug is taken—rock concert, nightclub, forest preserve, outdoors vs. indoors, etc.

Notes

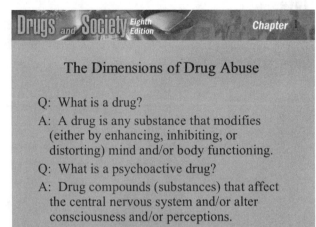

The Dimensions of Drug Abuse

Q: What is a drug?
A: A drug is any substance that modifies (either by enhancing, inhibiting, or distorting) mind and/or body functioning.
Q: What is a psychoactive drug?
A: Drug compounds (substances) that affect the central nervous system and/or alter consciousness and/or perceptions.

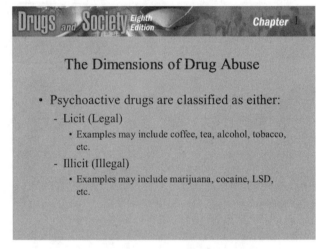

The Dimensions of Drug Abuse

- Psychoactive drugs are classified as either:
  - Licit (Legal)
    - Examples may include coffee, tea, alcohol, tobacco, etc.
  - Illicit (Illegal)
    - Examples may include marijuana, cocaine, LSD, etc.

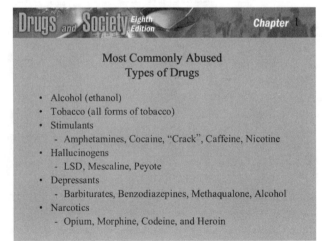

Most Commonly Abused
Types of Drugs

- Alcohol (ethanol)
- Tobacco (all forms of tobacco)
- Stimulants
  - Amphetamines, Cocaine, "Crack", Caffeine, Nicotine
- Hallucinogens
  - LSD, Mescaline, Peyote
- Depressants
  - Barbiturates, Benzodiazepines, Methaqualone, Alcohol
- Narcotics
  - Opium, Morphine, Codeine, and Heroin

Drugs and Society — Eighth Edition — Chapter 1

Most Commonly Abused Types of Drugs (continued)

- Cannabis
  - Marijuana and Hashish
- Inhalants/organic solvents
  - Inhalants such as gasoline, model glue, paint thinner, as well as certain foods, herbs, and vitamins

---

Drugs and Society — Eighth Edition — Chapter 1

Designer Drugs/Synthetic Drugs or Synthetic Opioids

- **Structural analogs** are drugs that result from altered chemical structures of current illicit drugs.
  - Involves modifying the basic molecular skeleton of a compound to form a new molecular species.

- **Designer drugs** are new categories of hybrid drugs
  - These relatively recent types of drugs are created as structural analogs of substances already classified under the Controlled Substances Act.

Drugs and Society — Eighth Edition — Chapter 1

Gateway Drugs

- **Gateway drugs** are types of drugs that are believed to lead to using other more powerfully mind-altering and addictive drugs, such as hallucinogens, cocaine, "crack", and heroin.
  - Alcohol, tobacco, and marijuana are the most commonly used gateway drugs.

Drugs and Society *Eighth Edition* — Chapter 1

Drug Misuse

- **Drug misuse** is the unintentional or inappropriate use of prescribed or over-the-counter (OTC) types of drugs.

Drugs and Society *Eighth Edition* — Chapter 1

Six Examples of Drug Misuse

- Taking more drugs than prescribed
- Using OTC or psychoactive drugs in excess without medical supervision
- Mixing drugs with alcohol or other types of drugs
- Using old medicines to self-treat new symptoms of an illness
- Discontinuing prescribed drugs at will and/or against physician's orders
- Administering prescribed drugs to a family member without medical consultation and supervision

Drugs and Society *Eighth Edition* — Chapter 1

Dimensions of Drug Abuse

- **Drug abuse** is the willful misuse of either licit or illicit drugs for the purpose of recreation, perceived necessity, or convenience.
  - Drug abuse refers to a more intense misuse of drugs -- often to the point of addiction
  - Often known as *chemical* or *substance* abuse

Drugs and Society Eighth Edition | Chapter

Erich Goode's Four Different Uses of Drugs

- Medical Use
- Legal Recreational Use
- Illegal Instrumental Use
- Illegal Recreational Use

Drugs and Society Eighth Edition | Chapter

Drug Use: Statistics and Trends

- Social drugs
  - $104 billion for alcohol
  - $51.9 billion for cigarettes
  - $2 billion for cigars; chewing, pipe, and roll-your-own tobacco; and snuff
  - $5.7 billion for coffee, teas, and cocoa
- Prescription drugs
  - $430 billion worldwide and $111.1 billion in the U.S.
- OTC drugs
  - $23.5 billion
- Miscellaneous drugs (such as aerosols, nutmeg, morning glory seeds, etc.)
  - Amount unknown

Drugs and Society Eighth Edition | Chapter

Drug Quiz (according to the research studies reported in your textbook)

Q: How many Americans, age 12 and up, have used alcohol in the past month?

A: 109 million

Q: How many Americans in the past month have smoked tobacco?

A: 56 million

Q: How many Americans use or have used marijuana in their lifetime?

A: 83 million (37%)

Q: The average household owns how many drugs?

A: 50 drugs (40% prescriptions, 60% OTC)

Notes

_____
_____
_____
_____
_____
_____
_____
_____
_____
_____
_____
_____
_____
_____
_____
_____
_____
_____
_____
_____
_____
_____
_____
_____
_____
_____
_____
_____
_____
_____
_____
_____
_____
_____

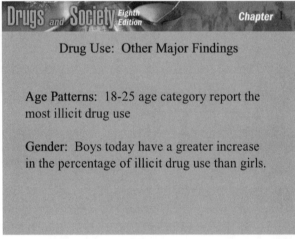

Drugs and Society *Eighth Edition* — Chapter 1

National Household Survey on Drug Abuse, 2001

- 184 million Americans used alcohol during their lifetime
- 152 million Americans used cigarettes
- 94 million Americans used any illicit drug(s)

Most commonly used illicit drugs (lifetime use):

- 37% used marijuana (4.8% used in last month)
- 13% used hallucinogens
- 16% used a psychotherapeutic drug(s) for non medical reason(s) (2.1% used in last month)
- 12.3% used cocaine

Drugs and Society *Eighth Edition* — Chapter 1

Drug Use: Other Major Findings

Age Patterns: 18-25 age category report the most illicit drug use

Gender: Boys today have a greater increase in the percentage of illicit drug use than girls.

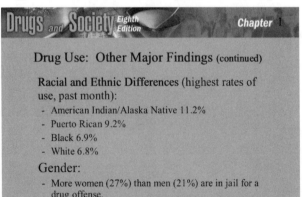

Drugs and Society *Eighth Edition* — Chapter 1

Drug Use: Other Major Findings (continued)

Racial and Ethnic Differences (highest rates of use, past month):

- American Indian/Alaska Native 11.2%
- Puerto Rican 9.2%
- Black 6.9%
- White 6.8%

Gender:

- More women (27%) than men (21%) are in jail for a drug offense.
- Women (24%) were also more than twice as likely as men (11%) to be in jail for fraud or theft.

Drug Use: Other Major Findings (continued)

Education: College graduates had the lowest rate of current use, while those who did not complete high school had the highest use of illicit drugs.

Employment: Unemployed persons have a greater tendency to use more illicit-types of drugs than people gainfully employed.

Drugs and Society Eighth Edition — Chapter 1

Three Types of Drug Users

- Experimenters
  - Begin using drugs largely because of peer pressure and curiosity, and they confine their use to recreational settings.
- Compulsive users
  - Devote considerable time and energy into getting high, talk incessantly (sometimes exclusively) about drug use, and become connoisseurs of street drugs.
- Floaters or "chippers"
  - Focus more on using other people's drugs without maintaining as much of a personal supply.

Drugs and Society Eighth Edition — Chapter 1

Why Are People So Attracted to Drugs?

- In search of pleasure or to heighten good feelings
- Temporarily relieve stress, tension, or anxiety
- Temporarily forget one's problems and avoid or postpone worries.
- Relax after a tension-filled day of work
- Fit in with peers or as a rite of passage
- Enhance religious or mystical experiences
- Relieve pain and some symptoms of illness

Drug Dependence

ÿ Both physical and psychological factors precipitate drug dependence:

- **Psychological dependence** refers to the need that a user may feel for continued use of a drug in order to experience its effects and/or relieve withdrawal symptoms.

- **Physical dependence** refers to the need to continue taking the drug to avoid withdrawal symptoms, which often include feelings of discomfort and illness.

Stages of Drug Dependence

- **Relief** - satisfaction from negative feelings in using the drug
- **Increased use** - involves taking greater quantities of the drug
- **Preoccupation** - consists of a constant concern with the substance
- **Dependency** - a synonym for addiction, is when more of the drug is sought despite the presence of physical symptoms
- **Withdrawal** - the physical and/or psychological effects from not using the drug

Costs of Drug Use to Society

- Shortened lifespan
- Broken home
- Fetal alcohol syndrome
- Criminal behavior
- Drugs in the workplace
- Cost of Assistance programs (e.g., Employee Assistance Programs [EAP's])
- Illness

Notes

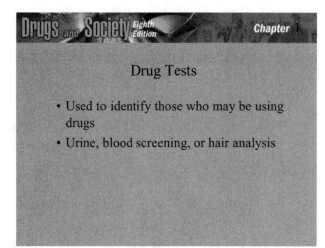

Drug Tests

- Used to identify those who may be using drugs
- Urine, blood screening, or hair analysis

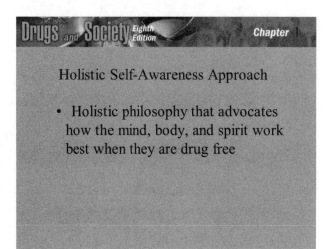

Holistic Self-Awareness Approach

- Holistic philosophy that advocates how the mind, body, and spirit work best when they are drug free

Notes

escape
depression

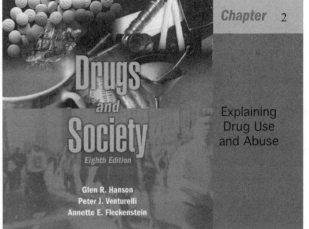

Why Do People Do Drugs?

- Why do people subject their bodies and minds to the harmful effects of repetitive drug use, eventual addiction, and relapse back into drug use?
- Why is drug use a more serious problem than in the past?

Seven Reasons Why Drug Use Is More Serious Today

- Since the 1960s drug use is more widespread
- Drugs are much more potent than they were years ago.
- Crack as well as crystal methamphetamine and other manufactured "newer" drugs offer potent effects at low cost.
- Illicit drug use remains extremely popular. Illicit drugs sales is a multibillion dollar a year business, with major influence on many national economies.

Notes

Seven Reasons Why Drug Use
Is More Serious Today

- Drug use endangers the future of a society by harming its youth and potentially destroying the lives of many young men and women.
- Drug use and especially drug dealing are becoming major factors in the growth of crime rates among the young.
- Seven in ten drug users work full-time and this increases the possibility of serious accidents in the workplace.

Basic Reasons People Take Drugs

- Searching for pleasure
- Relieve stress, tension, or depression
- Peer pressure
- Enhance religious or mystical experiences
- Enhance social experiences
- Enhance work performance
- Relieve pain or symptoms of illness
- Can you think of other reasons?

Nature of Addiction

- Should addiction be considered:
  - A bad habit?
  - A failure of healthy choices?
  - A failure of morality?
  - A symptom of other problems?
  - A chronic disease?

Notes

_____

_____

_____

_____

_____

_____

_____

_____

_____

_____

_____

_____

_____

_____

_____

_____

_____

_____

_____

_____

_____

_____

_____

_____

_____

_____

_____

_____

_____

_____

_____

_____

_____

_____

Drugs and Society Eighth Edition — Chapter 2

Cost of Addiction

- Although public perception of drug abuse and addiction as a major social problem has waxed and waned over the past 20 years, the social costs of addiction have not.
- The total criminal justice, health insurance, and other costs in the United States are roughly estimated at $90 to $185 billion annually.

Drugs and Society Eighth Edition — Chapter 2

Defining Addiction

- The term **addiction** is derived from the Latin verb *addicere*, which refers to the process of binding to things.
- Addiction is a complex disease. Originally, the World Health Organization (WHO) defined it as "a state of periodic or chronic intoxication detrimental to the individual and society, which is characterized by an overwhelming desire to continue taking the drug and to obtain it by any means" (1964, pp. 9-10).

Drugs and Society Eighth Edition — Chapter 2

The Term Addiction includes both Physical and Psychological Dependence

- Physical dependence is the body's need to constantly have the drug or drugs
- Psychological dependence is the mental inability to stop using the drug or drugs.

Drugs *and* Society Eighth Edition   Chapter 2

Substance Abuse and Dependence:
(from DSM-IV-TR, 4th Edition)

- While "substance abuse" is considered maladaptive, it is carefully differentiated from true addiction, called "substance dependence," the essential feature of which is continued use despite significant substance-related problems known to user.

Drugs *and* Society Eighth Edition   Chapter 2

Physical/Psychological Dependence

- Significant substance-related problems experienced by the user, includes:
  - Tolerance – need for increased usage
  - Withdrawal – unpleasant physical and/or emotional symptoms experienced by the user when attempting to quit using a drug
  - Compulsive - Increasing time spent in substance-related activities (obtaining and using, and recovering from drug effects)

[handwritten margin note:] withdraw - UNSUCCESSFUL attempts to cut down (body's attempt to withdraw)

[handwritten note:] KNOW definitions

Drugs *and* Society Eighth Edition   Chapter 2

Major Models of Addiction

- Moral model – poor morals and lifestyle – a choice
- Disease model – a belief that addiction is both chronic and progressive and that the drug user does not have control over the use and abuse of the drug
- Character or personality predisposition model – personality disorder - problems with the *personality* of the addicted

[handwritten note:] quizzed

Notes

Career Pattern of Addiction

- Experimentation or initiation of drug use
- Escalation (increasing use)
- Maintenance – optimistic belief that the drug fits in well with day-to-day goals
- Dysfunction – problems with use interfering with day-to-day goals
- Recovery – getting out of drug use/abuse
- Ex-Addict – successfully quitting

Some Major Risk Factors for Addiction

- Alcohol and/or other drugs used in order to help stress and/or anxiety
- Alcohol and/or other drugs used alone
- Availability of drugs
- Abusive and/or neglectful parents; other dysfunctional family patterns
- Misperception of peer norms regarding the extent of alcohol and/or drug use
- Alienation factors: isolation, emptiness, etc.

Major Risk Factors for Adolescents:

- Physical or sexual abuse (past and/or present)
- Peer norms in favor of drug use
- Misperception and/or power of age group peer norms
- Conflicts, such as dependence versus independence, adult maturational tasks versus fear, low self esteem, etc.

(handwritten note) LIKE ON the edge thing →

Drugs and Society — Eighth Edition — Chapter 2

Major Risk Factors for Adolescents
(continued)

- Teenage risk-taking, omnipotence, or invulnerability
- Cultural definition of use as a rite of passage into adulthood
- Cultural definition of use as glamorous, fun, etc.

Drugs and Society — Eighth Edition — Chapter 2

Major Risk Factors for Adults

- Disappointment when life's expectations are not met or realization of unattainable goals
- Retirement - loss of a meaningful role or occupational identity
- Loss, grief, or isolation - loss of parents, divorce, death of a spouse, or departure of children

Drugs and Society — Eighth Edition — Chapter 2

Biological Explanations for Use and Abuse of Drugs

- Genetic and biophysiological theories
  - Addiction is based on genes, brain dysfunction, and biochemical patterns
  - Biological explanations emphasize the Central Nervous System (CNS)
- Reward centers in some people are more sensitive to drugs resulting in more pleasure and greater rewarding experiences

Notes

3 THEORIES
- BIOLOGICAL
- PSYCHOLOGICAL
- SOCIOlogical

BIO -

MORE SENSITIVE TO
drugs

Abused drugs are
positive reinforce
ment
passed in genes

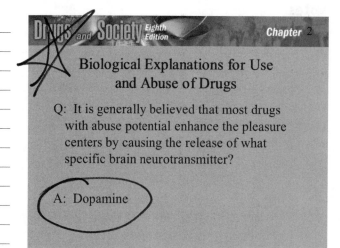

Biological Explanations for Use and Abuse of Drugs

Q: It is generally believed that most drugs with abuse potential enhance the pleasure centers by causing the release of what specific brain neurotransmitter?

A: Dopamine

Three Principal Biological Theories

- Abused drugs are positive reinforcers
- Drug abuse and psychiatric disorders
- Genetic explanations

based on genes

Genetic Explanations for Contribution to Drug Abuse Vulnerability

- Character traits, such as insecurity and vulnerability, may be genetically determined
- Factors that determine how difficult it will be to break a drug addiction may be genetically determined

Notes

Drugs and Society *Eighth Edition* — Chapter 2

Psychological Explanations for the Use and Abuse of Drugs

- The American Psychiatric Association classifies severe drug dependence as a form of <u>psychiatric disorder.</u>
- Drugs that are abused can cause mental conditions that mimic major psychiatric illness.
- It is sometimes difficult to distinguish between psychological and substance-related problems. Psychological problems primarily deal with mental or emotional states, often associated with or exacerbated by social and environmental factors

ex. schizophrenia

Drugs and Society *Eighth Edition* — Chapter 2

Psychological Explanations for the Use and Abuse of Drugs

- Psychological factors of addiction include:
  - escape from reality, boredom, inability to cope with anxiety, destructive self-indulgence (constantly desiring intoxicants), blind compliance with drug-abusing peers, self-destructiveness, and blindly using drugs without wanting to understand the harmful effects of drug use.

Drugs and Society *Eighth Edition* — Chapter 2

Theories Based on Learning

Memorable feeling attached to 1st use — "chasing the dragon"

- Conditioning - the close association of significant reinforcing stimulus with another less significant or neutral stimulus
- Habituation - repeating certain patterns of behavior until they become established or habitual
- "Addiction to pleasure" theory - assumes it is biologically normal to continue a pleasure stimulus when once begun

Notes

Who's at Risk?

new thrills

- People at the highest risk of drug use and addiction are known as drug sensation-seeking individuals or sensation-seekers.
  - These individuals continually search for new or novel thrills in their experiences, and are known to have a relentless desire to pursue physical and psychological stimulation often involving dangerous behavior.
  - Usually these types of individuals also maintain a constant preoccupation with getting high.

Drugs and Society Eighth Edition — Chapter 2

Social Psychological Learning Theories

- If the effects of drug use become personally rewarding, "or becomes reinforcing through conditioning, the chances of continuing to use are greater than stopping."
- Differential reinforcement

Drugs and Society Eighth Edition — Chapter 2

Sociological Explanations

- Social learning
- Role of significant others
- Labeling
- Subculture theory

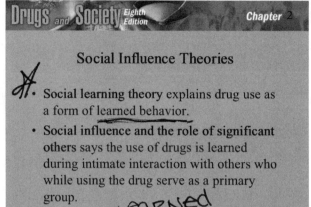

Social Influence Theories

- Social learning theory explains drug use as a form of learned behavior.
- Social influence and the role of significant others says the use of drugs is learned during intimate interaction with others who while using the drug serve as a primary group.

Learned behavior

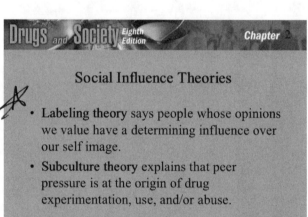

Social Influence Theories

- Labeling theory says people whose opinions we value have a determining influence over our self image.
- Subculture theory explains that peer pressure is at the origin of drug experimentation, use, and/or abuse.

easy to become deviant without social controls

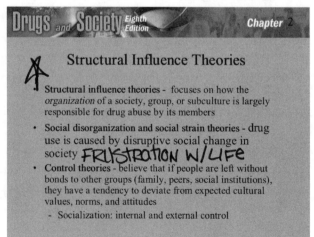

Structural Influence Theories

- Structural influence theories - focuses on how the *organization* of a society, group, or subculture is largely responsible for drug abuse by its members
- Social disorganization and social strain theories - drug use is caused by disruptive social change in society *FRUSTRATION W/LIFE*
- Control theories - believe that if people are left without bonds to other groups (family, peers, social institutions), they have a tendency to deviate from expected cultural values, norms, and attitudes
  - Socialization: internal and external control

Notes

Danger Signals of Drug Abuse

- Do those close to you often ask about your drug use? Have they noticed changes in your moods or behavior?
- Are you defensive if a friend or relative mentions your drug or alcohol use?
- Are you sometimes embarrassed or frightened by your behavior under the influence of drugs or alcohol?

Danger Signals of Drug Abuse

- Have you ever gone to see a new doctor because your regular physician would not prescribe the drug you wanted?
- When you are under pressure or feel anxious, do you automatically take a depressant, stimulant or drink?
- Do you take drugs more often or for purposes other than those recommended by your doctor?

Danger Signals of Drug Abuse

- Do you mix drugs and alcohol?
- Do you drink or take drugs regularly to help you sleep?
- Do you have to take drugs to relieve boredom or get through the day?
- Do you think you have a drug problem?

Drugs and Society *Eighth Edition*   **Chapter** 2

Low-Risk and High Risk Drug Choices

- **Low risk drug choices** refer to values and attitudes that lead to controlling the use of alcohol or drugs – self-monitoring your drug use behavior and abstinence.
- **High risk drug choices** refer to developing values and attitudes that lead to using drugs both habitually and addictively – constantly searching for drinking and drug parties, hanging with drug abusers, etc., etc.

Need to know for quiz:
4 reasons why drug use is serious
    moral/social LEARNING theory of addiction
    why people are attracted to drugs
    dopamine - neurotransmitter
    3 types of drug users
    4 factors of drug use

Chapter 3: Drug Use, Regulation, and the Law

Notes

Drug Use, Regulation, and the Law

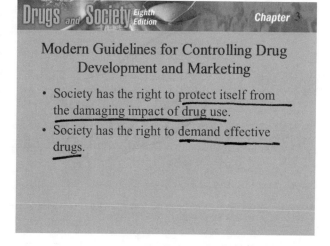

Modern Guidelines for Controlling Drug Development and Marketing

- Society has the right to protect itself from the damaging impact of drug use.
- Society has the right to demand effective drugs.

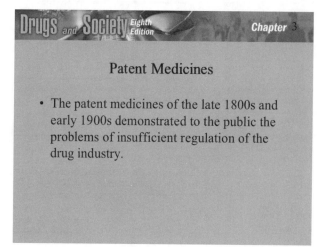

Patent Medicines

- The patent medicines of the late 1800s and early 1900s demonstrated to the public the problems of insufficient regulation of the drug industry.

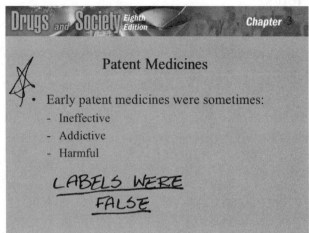

Patent Medicines

- Early patent medicines were sometimes:
  - Ineffective
  - Addictive
  - Harmful

LABELS WERE FALSE

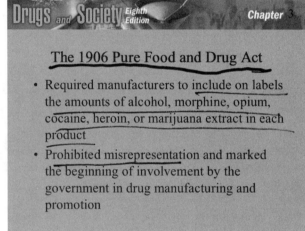

The 1906 Pure Food and Drug Act

- Required manufacturers to include on labels the amounts of alcohol, morphine, opium, cocaine, heroin, or marijuana extract in each product
- Prohibited misrepresentation and marked the beginning of involvement by the government in drug manufacturing and promotion

1st drug law

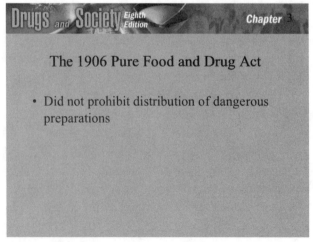

The 1906 Pure Food and Drug Act

- Did not prohibit distribution of dangerous preparations

Notes

went on 4 6 years

court case -
cancer patient

COMPANIES
had to FILE FORMS VERIFYING
their safety

antibiotics too little
barbituates too much
were MISUSED

Drugs and Society *Eighth Edition* **Chapter 3**

~~went on f~~

The Sherley Amendment in 1912

- Manufacturers' therapeutic claims were not controlled by the Pure Food and Drug Act.
- The Sherley Amendment in 1912 was passed to strengthen existing law and required that labels should not contain "any statement...regarding the curative or therapeutic effect...which is false and fraudulent."

Drugs and Society *Eighth Edition* **Chapter 3**

Federal Food, Drug and Cosmetic Act 1938

- All nonnarcotic drugs were available OTC prior to World War II.
- Drug safety was not covered in existing law.
- The sale and use of Elixir Sulfanilamide led to a tragic accident that killed over 100 people. SOLVENT used w/ drug was TOXIC

Drugs and Society *Eighth Edition* **Chapter 3**

Federal Food, Drug, and Cosmetic Act

- Defined drugs to include products that affect bodily structure or function even in the absence of disease
- Allowed the manufacturer to determine whether drug was to be labeled prescription or nonprescription

establishing criteria still in use today

concerned about drug companies profits

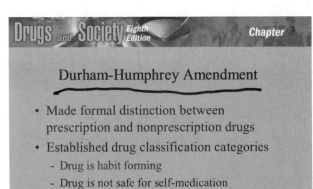

Durham-Humphrey Amendment

- Made formal distinction between prescription and nonprescription drugs
- Established drug classification categories
  - Drug is habit forming
  - Drug is not safe for self-medication
  - Drug is a new drug and not shown to be completely safe

Kefauver-Harris Amendment

- Consequence of thalidomide tragedy
- Drug manufacturers had to demonstrate the efficacy and safety of drugs
- The FDA was empowered to withdraw approval of a drug that was already being marketed
- The FDA regulated and evaluated drug testing by pharmaceutical companies

Regulating New Drug Development

- The amended federal Food, Drug, and Cosmetic Act in force today requires that all new drugs be registered with and approved by the FDA.

phase 1 = 20-100 volunteers
(usually med students)
MONITOR dosage +
side effects

phase 2 = CLINICAL phase
100-300 volunteers
(patents w/ medical
problems)
dosage + effects

phase 3 = MARKETING, KNOW
(if there are
problems, change
dosages
wide basis

post marketing still
a period of surveillence
bcuz some side
effects dont show
up for years

need to KNOW steps

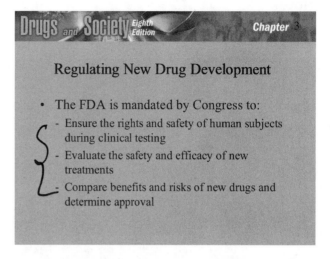

Regulating New Drug Development

- The FDA is mandated by Congress to:
  - Ensure the rights and safety of human subjects during clinical testing
  - Evaluate the safety and efficacy of new treatments
  - Compare benefits and risks of new drugs and determine approval

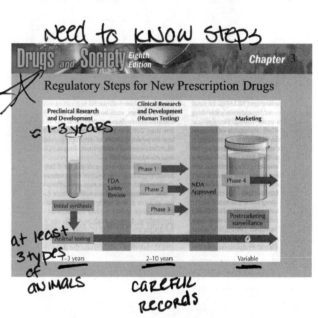

Regulatory Steps for New Prescription Drugs

1-3 years

at least 3 types of animals

careful records

Regulatory Steps for New Prescription Drugs

- Step 1. Preclinical research and development
- Step 2. Clinical research and development
  - Initial clinical stage
  - Clinical pharmacological evaluation stage
  - Extended clinical evaluation
- Step 3. Permission to market
  - Postmarketing surveillance

Notes

Exceptions:
Special Drug-Marketing Laws

- "Fast-track" rule
  - Applied to testing of certain drugs for rate cancers, AZT, etc.
- Orphan Drug Law
  - Tax advantages for development of drugs to treat "rare diseases" since this can be otherwise unprofitable
- Prescription Drug User Fee Act of 1992
  - Increase reviewers and decrease review time

The Regulation of
Nonprescription Drugs

- In 1972, the FDA initiated a program to evaluate the effectiveness and safety of nonprescription drugs
- The FDA evaluated each active ingredient in OTC medications and placed ingredients into three categories:
  - Safe and effective
  - Not safe and effective or unacceptable indications
  - Insufficient data to permit final classification

Switching Policy

- The drug must have been used by prescription for 3 years.
- Use must have been relatively high during the time it was used by prescription.
- Adverse drug reactions must not be alarming, and the frequency of side effects must not have increased during the time the drug was available to the public.

Prescription Advertising

- The majority of prescription drug promotion is directed at health professionals and controlled by the FDA.

Pg 96-97 ### The Harrison Act 1914

- First federal legislation to regulate and control the production, importation, sale, purchase, and free distribution of opium or drugs derived from opium. (narcotics)

The Comprehensive Drug Abuse Prevention and Control Act of 1970

- This act divided substances with abuse potential into categories based on the degree of their abuse potential and clinical usefulness
- Schedules I, II, III, IV, V

(handwritten notes, left side)

LSD
HEROINE

NOT REFILLED demEROL
UNLESS SEEN MORPHINE
by doctor cocaine

✓ PRESCRIPTIONS

Drugs and Society Eighth Edition — Chapter 3

"Scheduling"

- Schedule I substances have high-abuse potential and no currently approved medicinal uses; they cannot be prescribed.
- Schedule II substances have high-abuse potential but are approved for medical uses and can be prescribed.
- Schedule III-V reflects the likelihood of abuse and clinical usefulness.

(handwritten) 3-5 MAY REFILL UP TO 5 TIMES

Drugs and Society Eighth Edition — Chapter 3

Drug Laws and Deterrence

- The increase in illegal drug use and drug addiction that began in the 1960s forced society to evaluate its view of drugs.

Drugs and Society Eighth Edition — Chapter 3

Drug Laws and Deterrence

- If a person abuses a drug, should he or she be treated as a criminal or as a sick person inflicted with a disease?

Drug Laws and Deterrence

- How is the user (supposedly the victim) distinguished from the pusher (supposedly the criminal) of an illicit drug, and who should be more harshly punished?

Drugs and Society Eighth Edition · Chapter 3

Drug Laws and Deterrence

- Are the laws and associated penalties effective deterrents against drug use or abuse, and how is effectiveness determined?

Drugs and Society Eighth Edition · Chapter 3

Strategies for Preventing Drug Abuse

- Supply reduction
  - Using drug laws to control the manufacturing and distribution of classified drugs

---

Strategies for Preventing Drug Abuse

Drugs and Society Eighth Edition — Chapter 3

- Demand reduction strategy
  - Aims to reduce the actual demand for drugs by working mainly with youth and teaching them to resist drugs

Suggestions for Reducing Demand

Drugs and Society Eighth Edition — Chapter 3

- A top priority of prevention is to reduce demand by youth.
- Education must be carefully designed for the target population.
- Attitudes toward drug abuse must be changed.
- Replacement therapy can be useful.

Strategies for Preventing Drug Abuse

Drugs and Society Eighth Edition — Chapter 3

- Inoculation
  - Aims to protect drug users by teaching them responsibility and explaining the effects of drugs on bodily and mental functioning

Drugs and Society *Eighth Edition* Chapter 3

Drug Courts

- Designed to deal with nonviolent, drug-abusing offenders

- Integrate mandatory drug testing, substance abuse treatment, sanctions, and incentives in a judicially supervised setting

- Provide support to rebuild lives

- Have had a positive impact

MIDTERM (opinion)

Drugs and Society *Eighth Edition* Chapter 3

Drug Legalization Debate

- Violence and crime would decrease/increase?
- Profits associated with illegal trade would decrease/increase?
- Law enforcement costs would decrease/increase?
- Addiction would decrease/increase?

Drugs and Society *Eighth Edition* Chapter 3

Drug Legalization Debate

- Societal/health costs would decrease/increase?
- Consumption would increase/decrease?

Drugs and Society Eighth Edition Chapter 3

Areas of Compromise?

- Selective legalization?
- Control through prescription or special outlets?
- Discretionary enforcement of drug laws?

Drugs and Society Eighth Edition Chapter 3

Drug Testing

- In response to the demand by society to stop the spread of drug abuse and its adverse consequences, drug testing has been implemented in some situations to detect drug users.

Drugs and Society Eighth Edition Chapter 3

Drug Testing

- Common types of drug testing include:
  - Breathalyzers
  - Urine, blood, and hair specimens

Drugs and Society Eighth Edition   Chapter 3

Pragmatic Drug Policies

- Government must develop programs that are consistent with the desires of the majority of the population.

Drugs and Society Eighth Edition   Chapter 3

Pragmatic Drug Policies

- Programs must de-emphasize interdiction and stress programs that reduce demand.
- Government and society must better understand how laws, used properly and selectively, can reinforce and communicate expected social behavior and values.

Drugs and Society Eighth Edition   Chapter 3

Pragmatic Drug Policies

- Programs such as antismoking campaigns should be implemented that employ "public consensus" more effectively.

Chapter 4: Homeostatic Systems and Drugs

Notes

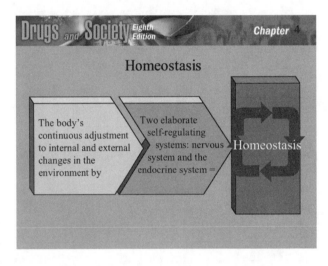

Homeostasis

The body's continuous adjustment to internal and external changes in the environment by

Two elaborate self-regulating systems: nervous system and the endocrine system =

Homeostasis

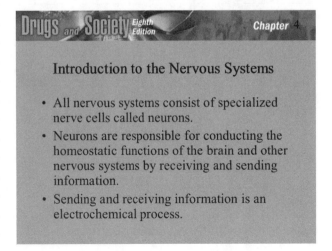

Introduction to the Nervous Systems

- All nervous systems consist of specialized nerve cells called neurons.
- Neurons are responsible for conducting the homeostatic functions of the brain and other nervous systems by receiving and sending information.
- Sending and receiving information is an electrochemical process.

Notes

N

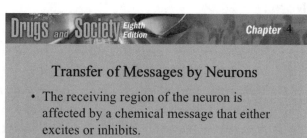

Transfer of Messages by Neurons

- The receiving region of the neuron is affected by a chemical message that either excites or inhibits.
- If the message is excitatory, an impulse moves from the receiving region of the neuron down the axon to the sending region, the terminal, and chemical messengers, neurotransmitters, are released.

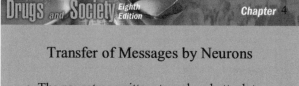

Transfer of Messages by Neurons

- The neurotransmitters travel and attach to receiving proteins called receptors on the target cells.
- Activation of receptors by neurotransmitters causes a change in the activity of the target cell; the target cells can be other neurons or cells that make up organs, muscles, or glands.

Sending Messages by Neurons

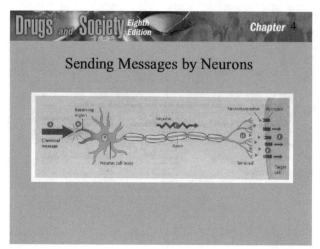

Notes

SEND OR RECEIVE
Messages

get an idea
of what
they all
do

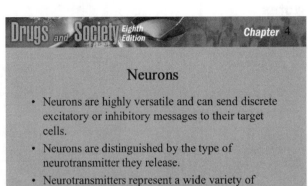

Neurons

- Neurons are highly versatile and can send discrete excitatory or inhibitory messages to their target cells.
- Neurons are distinguished by the type of neurotransmitter they release.
- Neurotransmitters represent a wide variety of chemical substances and functions.
  - Example: dopamine activates the pleasure center

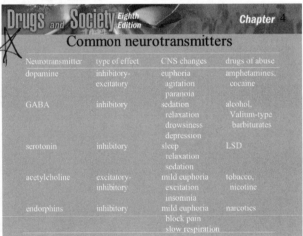

Common neurotransmitters

Neurotransmitter	type of effect	CNS changes	drugs of abuse
dopamine	inhibitory-excitatory	euphoria agitation paranoia	amphetamines, cocaine
GABA	inhibitory	sedation relaxation drowsiness depression	alcohol, Valium-type barbiturates
serotonin	inhibitory	sleep relaxation sedation	LSD
acetylcholine	excitatory-inhibitory	mild euphoria excitation insomnia	tobacco, nicotine
endorphins	inhibitory	mild euphoria block pain slow respiration	narcotics

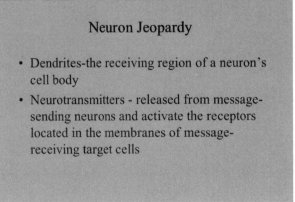

Neuron Jeopardy

- Dendrites-the receiving region of a neuron's cell body
- Neurotransmitters - released from message-sending neurons and activate the receptors located in the membranes of message-receiving target cells

Notes

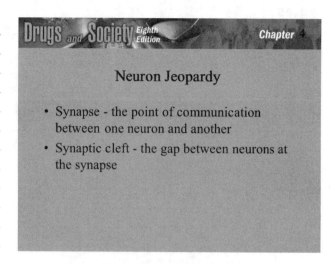

Neuron Jeopardy

- Synapse - the point of communication between one neuron and another
- Synaptic cleft - the gap between neurons at the synapse

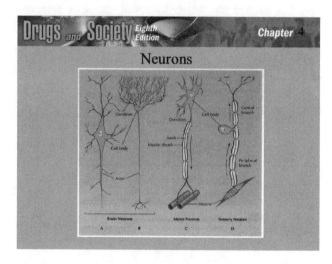

Neurons

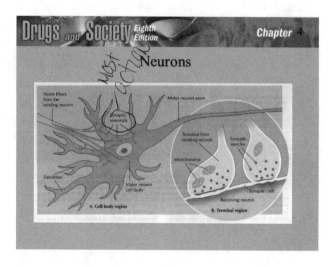

Neurons

Notes

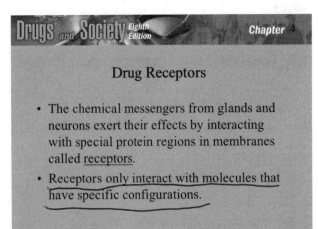

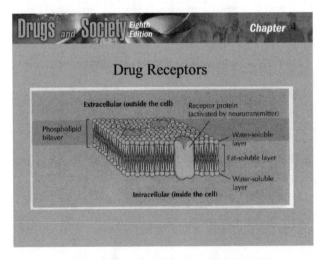

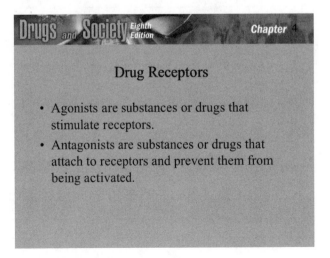

Notes

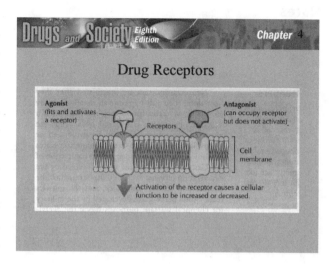

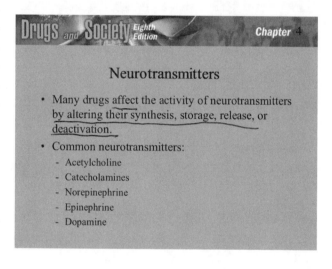

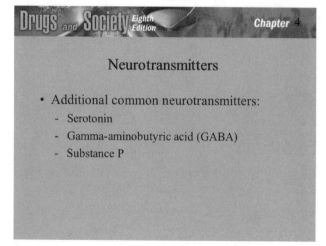

Drugs and Society *Eighth Edition* **Chapter** 4

Major Divisions of the Nervous System

- Two major components of the nervous system
  - Central nervous system (CNS)
  - Peripheral nervous system (PNS)
- CNS
  - Brain
  - Spinal cord
- CNS receives information from PNS, evaluates information, then regulates muscle and organ activity via PNS

Drugs and Society *Eighth Edition* **Chapter** 4

Central and Autonomic Nervous Systems

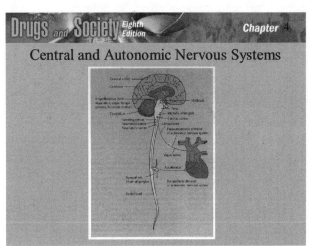

Drugs and Society *Eighth Edition* **Chapter** 4

Central Nervous System

- Reticular activating system
  - Receives input from all the sensory systems and cerebral cortex
  - Control's the brain's state of arousal
- The basal ganglia
  - Primarily responsible for controlling motoring activity
- The limbic system
  - Regulates mood and mental states
  - Dopamine

Handwritten notes:

12 PAIRS OF NERVES IN BRAIN

31 PAIRS OF NERVES IN NERVOUS SYSTEM

things that happen to basal effect limbic

SenSe of Mating, caRing for young

Notes

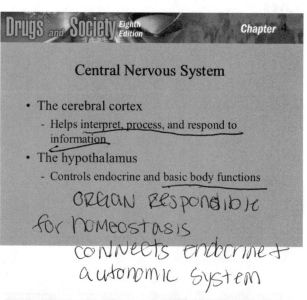

Central Nervous System

- The cerebral cortex
  - Helps interpret, process, and respond to information
- The hypothalamus
  - Controls endocrine and basic body functions

ORGAN RESPONSIBLE for HOMEOSTASIS connects endocrine + autonomic System

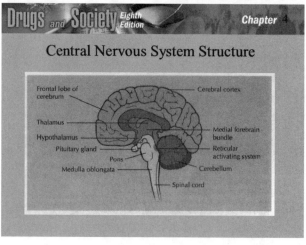

Central Nervous System Structure

Frontal lobe of cerebrum — Cerebral cortex
Thalamus
Hypothalamus — Medial forebrain bundle
Pituitary gland — Reticular activating system
Pons
Medulla oblongata — Cerebellum
Spinal cord

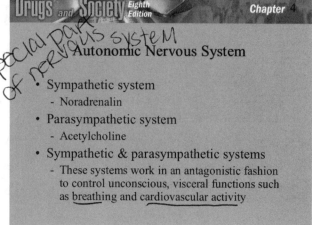

special part of nervous system

Autonomic Nervous System

- Sympathetic system
  - Noradrenalin
- Parasympathetic system
  - Acetylcholine
- Sympathetic & parasympathetic systems
  - These systems work in an antagonistic fashion to control unconscious, visceral functions such as breathing and cardiovascular activity

Notes

_____

neurons - nervous system

hormones - endocrine system

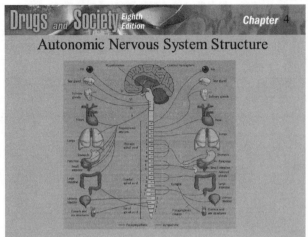

Autonomic Nervous System Structure

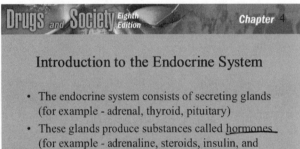

Introduction to the Endocrine System

- The endocrine system consists of secreting glands (for example - adrenal, thyroid, pituitary)
- These glands produce substances called hormones (for example - adrenaline, steroids, insulin, and sex hormones)
- These substances are information transferring molecules

Introduction to the Endocrine System

- Hormones are secreted into the bloodstream and carried by the blood to all the organs and tissues of the body.
- Hormones affect selected tissues that are designed to receive the information.
- Hormones may be highly selective or very general with regard to the cells or organs they influence.

Notes

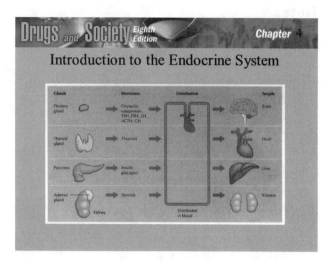

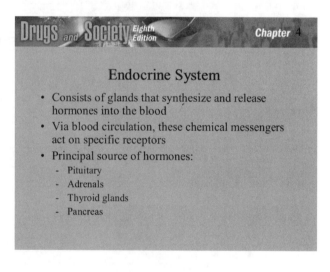

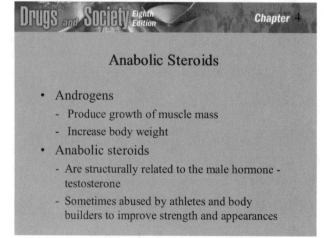

Notes

increase in dopamine in scitzos causes hallucanations

addiction = disease of the brain

- *Better def of addiction*
- *impaired control over* ← *use of a drug*

- *50 NEUROTRANSMITTERS*
- *abused drugs take same STRUCTURE as NEUROTRANS-MITTERS*

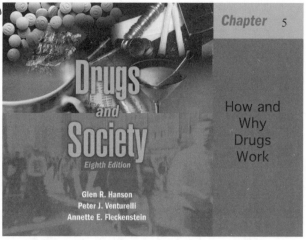

Drugs and Society Eighth Edition — Chapter 5

Intended and Unintended Effects of Drugs

- Intended responses
  - reason for using the drug
- Unintended responses
  - side effects
- The main distinction between intended and side effects depends on the therapeutic objective

---

Drugs and Society Eighth Edition — Chapter 5

Common Side Effects of Drugs

- Nausea or vomiting
- Changes in mental alertness
- Dependence
  - Withdrawal
- Allergic reactions
- Changes in cardiovascular activity

Notes

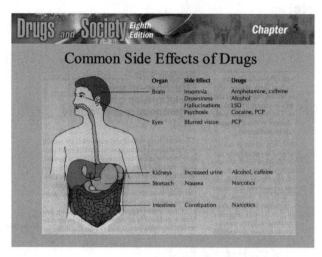

Common Side Effects of Drugs

Organ	Side Effect	Drugs
Brain	Insomnia	Amphetamine, caffeine
	Drowsiness	Alcohol
	Hallucinations	LSD
	Psychosis	Cocaine, PCP
Eyes	Blurred vision	PCP
Kidneys	Increased urine	Alcohol, caffeine
Stomach	Nausea	Narcotics
Intestines	Constipation	Narcotics

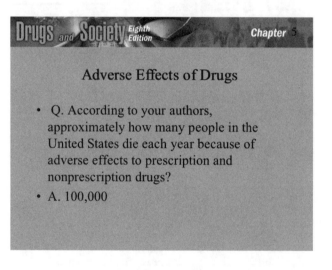

Adverse Effects of Drugs

- Q. According to your authors, approximately how many people in the United States die each year because of adverse effects to prescription and nonprescription drugs?
- A. 100,000

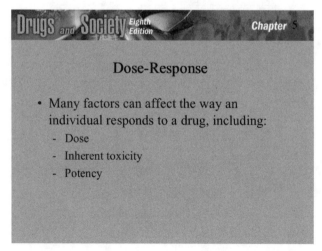

Dose-Response

- Many factors can affect the way an individual responds to a drug, including:
  - Dose
  - Inherent toxicity
  - Potency

ORGANS EFFECT METABOLIZISM
 LIVER
 KIDNEYS

FACTORS
 ADMINISTRATION
 ABSORPTION
 DISTRIBUTION

 BIOACTIVATION

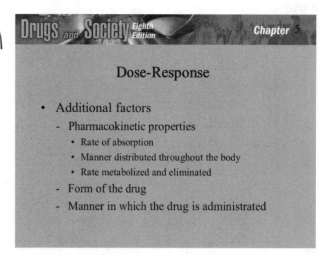

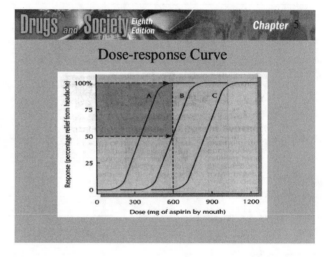

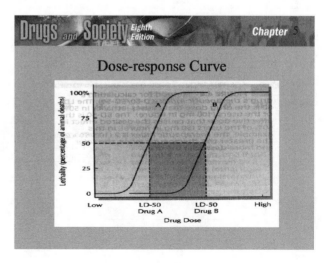

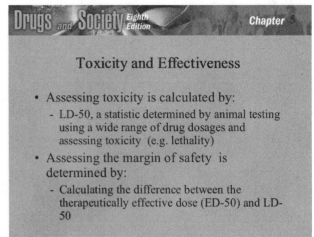

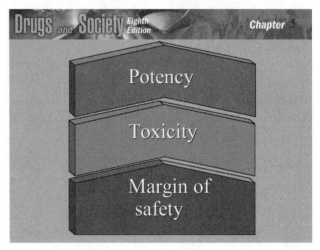

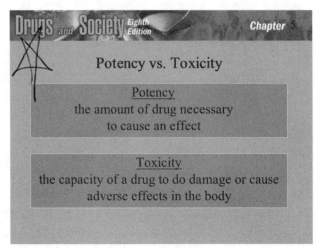

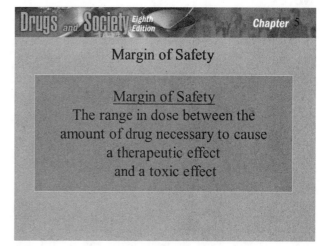

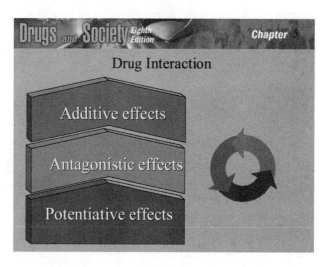

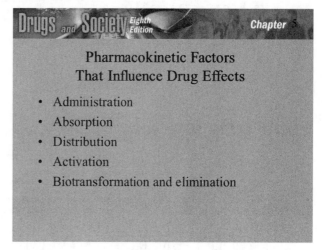

Notes

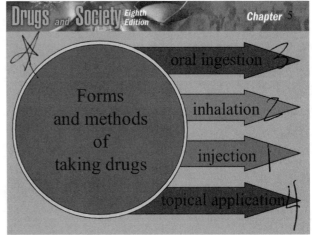

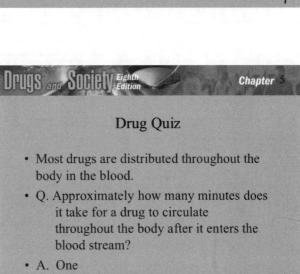

water soluable drugs
can Not pass through
blood brain - the barrier, fat
soluable can
placental barrier does Not
let large MOLECULES pass
through, small MOLECULES
can

Drugs and Society *Eighth Edition*   Chapter 5

Define the Following

- Threshold dose - the minimum amount of a drug necessary to have an effect
- Plateau effect - the maximum effect a drug can have regardless of the dose
- Cumulative effect - the buildup of drug concentration in the body due to multiple doses taken within short intervals

Drugs and Society *Eighth Edition*   Chapter 5

Biotransformation

- Is the process of changing the chemical or pharmacological properties of a drug by metabolism
- The liver is the major organ that metabolizes drugs in the body
  - Induction
  - Tolerance
- The kidney is the next most important organ for drug elimination

TERATOGENIC ~
CAUSING abNORMAL
physical developMENT IN
the FETUS

Drugs and Society *Eighth Edition*   Chapter 5

Physiological Variables That Modify Drug Effects

- Age
- Gender MORE SIMILARITIES THAN DIFFERENCES
- Pregnancy

★ REBOUND - opposite
effect that drug
normally produces

Drugs and **Society** *Eighth Edition*   Chapter 5

Adaptive Processes

- Tolerance - changes causing decreased response to a set dose of a drug
- Dependence - the physiological and psychological changes or adaptations that occur in response to the frequent administration of a drug
- Withdrawal

Drugs and **Society** *Eighth Edition*   Chapter 5

Adaptive Processes

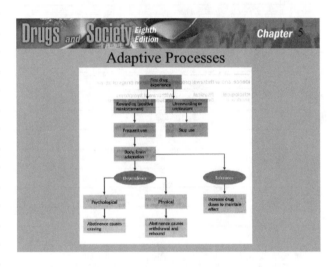

Drugs and **Society** *Eighth Edition*   Chapter 5

Tolerance to Drugs

- Drug disposition tolerance
- Pharmaco-dynamic tolerance
- Reverse tolerance
- Cross-tolerance

Cross dependence -
using treating withdrawl
symptoms w/ similar
feeling drugs
ex. heroine → methadone

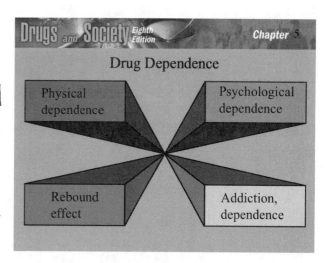

Drug Dependence

- Physical dependence
- Psychological dependence
- Rebound effect
- Addiction, dependence

Chapter 5

Addiction and Abuse

- The term addiction has many meanings. It is often used interchangeably with dependence, either physiological or psychological in nature; or other times, it is used synonymously with the term drug abuse.

Chapter 5

Psychological Dependence

- Psychological dependence occurs because drug use is rewarding, produces euphoria, increases energy and relaxation, or because it produces cravings.

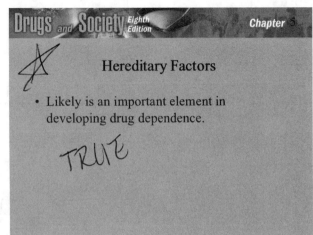

Placebo Effect

Inactive compound
where mind over
body happens

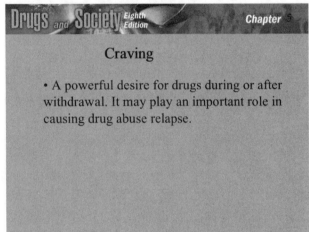

Notes

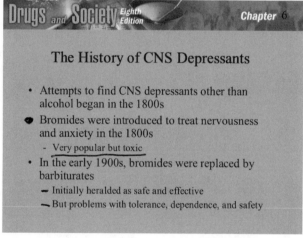

The History of CNS Depressants

- Attempts to find CNS depressants other than alcohol began in the 1800s
- Bromides were introduced to treat nervousness and anxiety in the 1800s
  - Very popular but toxic
- In the early 1900s, bromides were replaced by barbiturates
  - Initially heralded as safe and effective
  - But problems with tolerance, dependence, and safety

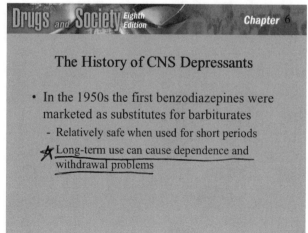

The History of CNS Depressants

- In the 1950s the first benzodiazepines were marketed as substitutes for barbiturates
  - Relatively safe when used for short periods
  - Long-term use can cause dependence and withdrawal problems

Notes

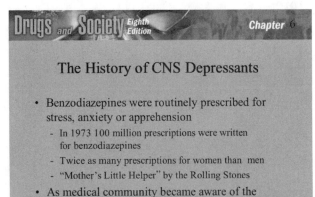

The History of CNS Depressants

- Benzodiazepines were routinely prescribed for stress, anxiety or apprehension
  - In 1973 100 million prescriptions were written for benzodiazepines
  - Twice as many prescriptions for women than men
  - "Mother's Little Helper" by the Rolling Stones
- As medical community became aware of the problem, use of depressants declined

1984 - 70 MILLION

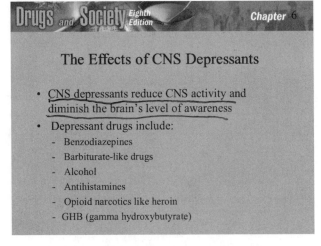

The Effects of CNS Depressants

- CNS depressants reduce CNS activity and diminish the brain's level of awareness
- Depressant drugs include:
  - Benzodiazepines
  - Barbiturate-like drugs
  - Alcohol
  - Antihistamines
  - Opioid narcotics like heroin
  - GHB (gamma hydroxybutyrate)

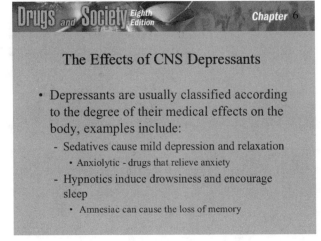

The Effects of CNS Depressants

- Depressants are usually classified according to the degree of their medical effects on the body, examples include:
  - Sedatives cause mild depression and relaxation
    - Anxiolytic - drugs that relieve anxiety
  - Hypnotics induce drowsiness and encourage sleep
    - Amnesiac can cause the loss of memory

Drugs *and* **Society** *Eighth Edition*   *Chapter* 6

The Effects of CNS Depressants

- The clinical value of CNS depressants is dose dependent
  - Low dose (sedatives, relieve anxiety and promote relaxation)
  - Higher doses (hypnotics, can cause drowsiness and promote sleep)
  - At even higher doses (anesthetics, can cause anesthesia and are used for patient management during surgery)

Drugs *and* **Society** *Eighth Edition*   *Chapter* 6

Types of CNS Depressants

Benzodiazepines: Valium-Type drugs
  - Prescribed for anxiety and sleep
  - 4 of the top-selling prescription drugs in the U.S.
    - Xanax, Halcion, Ativan, diazepam
- Medical uses
  - Relief from anxiety, neurosis, muscle relaxation, alleviation of lower-back pain, treatment of convulsive disorders, induction of sleep, relief from withdrawal symptoms, induction of amnesia

Drugs *and* **Society** *Eighth Edition*   *Chapter* 6

Types of CNS Depressants

- Mechanisms of action for benzodiazepine
  - Affect neurons that have receptors for the neurotransmitter - GABA
- GABA - inhibitory transmitter in brain regions
  - Limbic system (alter mood)
  - RAS (cause drowsiness)
  - Motor cortex (relax muscles)

Notes

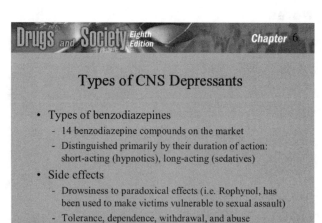

Types of CNS Depressants

- Types of benzodiazepines
  - 14 benzodiazepine compounds on the market
  - Distinguished primarily by their duration of action: short-acting (hypnotics), long-acting (sedatives)
- Side effects
  - Drowsiness to paradoxical effects (i.e. Rophynol, has been used to make victims vulnerable to sexual assault)
  - Tolerance, dependence, withdrawal, and abuse

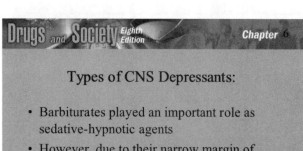

Types of CNS Depressants:

- Barbiturates played an important role as sedative-hypnotic agents
- However, due to their narrow margin of safety and their abuse liability, they were replaced by benzodiazepines
  - Caused many negative side effects from nausea to death from respiratory or cardiovascular depression

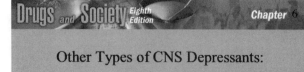

Other Types of CNS Depressants:

- Methaqualone
- Glutethimide
- Methyprylon
- Chloral hydrate
- Ethchlorvynol
- Antihistamines
- GHB (gamma hydroxybutyrate)

Drugs and **Society** *Eighth Edition*   Chapter 6

Patterns of Abuse With CNS Depressants

- The American Psychiatric Association considers dependence on CNS depressants a psychiatric disorder

Drugs and **Society** *Eighth Edition*   Chapter 6

Patterns of Abuse With CNS Depressants

People most likely to abuse CNS depressants include individuals who:
- Use drugs to relieve continual stress
- Paradoxically feel euphoria and stimulation from depressants
- Use depressants to counteract the unpleasant effects of other drugs of abuse
- Combine depressants with alcohol and heroin to potentiate the effects

Drugs and **Society** *Eighth Edition*   Chapter 6

Patterns of Abuse With CNS Depressants

- Detoxification - is the elimination of a toxic substance, such as a drug, and its effects
  - With CNS depressants, this is achieved by substituting a long-acting barbiturate or benzodiazepine for the offending CNS depressant

ANXIETY DISORDER

PANIC DISORDER - COMES ON W/O KNOWING

OBSESSIVE/COMPULSIVE DISORDER - Repeated thoughts
or behaviors that
are UNWANTED

Post Traumatic Stress Disorder -

A Phobia - social or specific phobia

General Anxiety Disorder

Chapter 7: Alcohol: Pharmacological Effects

Notes

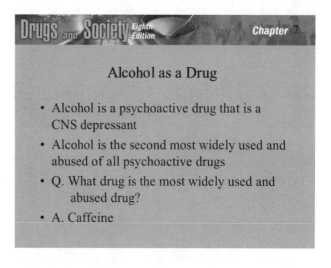

Alcohol as a Drug

- Alcohol is a psychoactive drug that is a CNS depressant
- Alcohol is the second most widely used and abused of all psychoactive drugs
- Q. What drug is the most widely used and abused drug?
- A. Caffeine

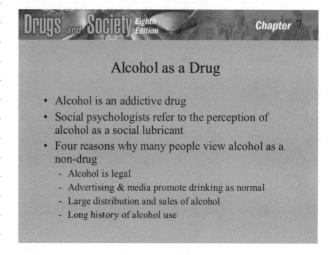

Alcohol as a Drug

- Alcohol is an addictive drug
- Social psychologists refer to the perception of alcohol as a social lubricant
- Four reasons why many people view alcohol as a non-drug
  - Alcohol is legal
  - Advertising & media promote drinking as normal
  - Large distribution and sales of alcohol
  - Long history of alcohol use

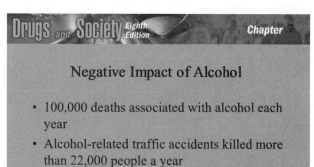

Negative Impact of Alcohol

- 100,000 deaths associated with alcohol each year
- Alcohol-related traffic accidents killed more than 22,000 people a year

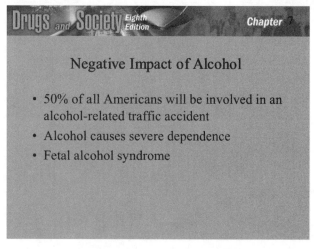

Negative Impact of Alcohol

- 50% of all Americans will be involved in an alcohol-related traffic accident
- Alcohol causes severe dependence
- Fetal alcohol syndrome

Negative Impact of Alcohol

- Disrupts personal, family, social, and professional functioning
- Illness, accidents, violence, and crime related to alcohol use
- Approximately $140 billion are spent annually dealing with social and health problems related to alcohol use

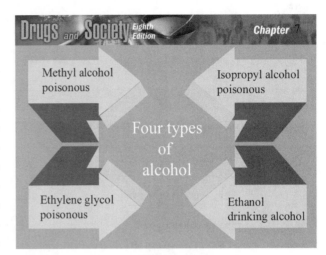

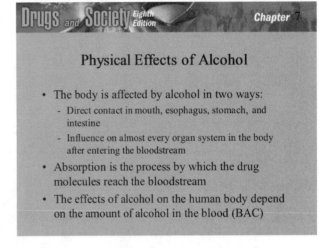

Physical Effects of Alcohol

- The body is affected by alcohol in two ways:
  - Direct contact in mouth, esophagus, stomach, and intestine
  - Influence on almost every organ system in the body after entering the bloodstream
- Absorption is the process by which the drug molecules reach the bloodstream
- The effects of alcohol on the human body depend on the amount of alcohol in the blood (BAC)

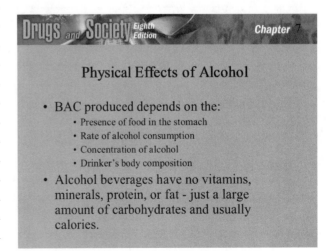

Physical Effects of Alcohol

- BAC produced depends on the:
  - Presence of food in the stomach
  - Rate of alcohol consumption
  - Concentration of alcohol
  - Drinker's body composition
- Alcohol beverages have no vitamins, minerals, protein, or fat - just a large amount of carbohydrates and usually calories.

Notes

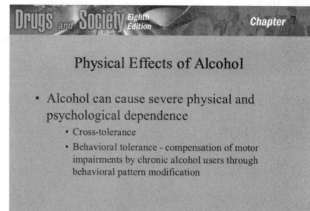

Physical Effects of Alcohol

- Alcohol can cause severe physical and psychological dependence
  - Cross-tolerance
  - Behavioral tolerance - compensation of motor impairments by chronic alcohol users through behavioral pattern modification

Blood Alcohol Level

- Almost 95% of the consumed alcohol is inactivated by liver metabolism.
- The liver metabolizes alcohol at a slow and constant rate and is unaffected by the amount ingested.
- Thus, if one can of beer is consumed each hour, the blood alcohol level (BAL) will remain constant.

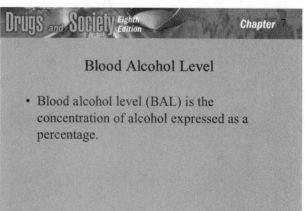

Blood Alcohol Level

- Blood alcohol level (BAL) is the concentration of alcohol expressed as a percentage.

Notes

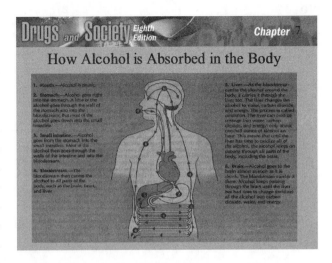

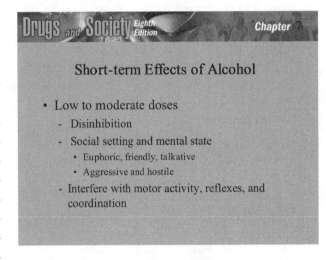

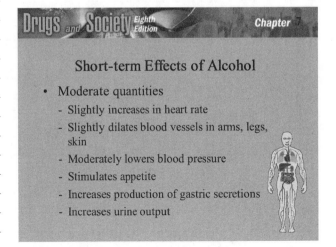

Notes

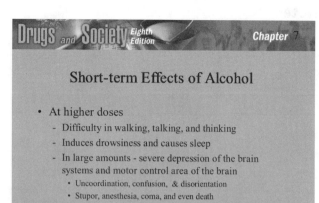

Short-term Effects of Alcohol

- At higher doses
  - Difficulty in walking, talking, and thinking
  - Induces drowsiness and causes sleep
  - In large amounts - severe depression of the brain systems and motor control area of the brain
    - Uncoordination, confusion, & disorientation
    - Stupor, anesthesia, coma, and even death
- Lethal level of alcohol is between 0.4 and 0.6% by volume in the blood

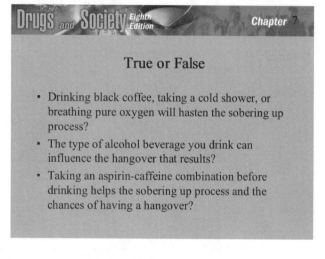

True or False

- Drinking black coffee, taking a cold shower, or breathing pure oxygen will hasten the sobering up process?
- The type of alcohol beverage you drink can influence the hangover that results?
- Taking an aspirin-caffeine combination before drinking helps the sobering up process and the chances of having a hangover?

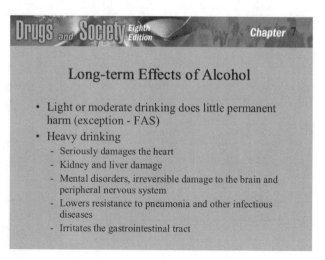

Long-term Effects of Alcohol

- Light or moderate drinking does little permanent harm (exception - FAS)
- Heavy drinking
  - Seriously damages the heart
  - Kidney and liver damage
  - Mental disorders, irreversible damage to the brain and peripheral nervous system
  - Lowers resistance to pneumonia and other infectious diseases
  - Irritates the gastrointestinal tract

Notes

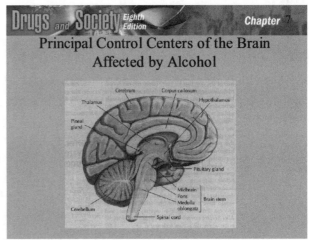

Principal Control Centers of the Brain Affected by Alcohol

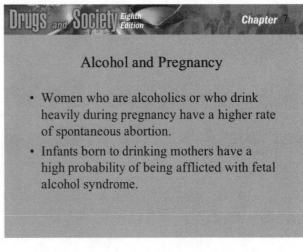

Alcohol and Pregnancy

- Women who are alcoholics or who drink heavily during pregnancy have a higher rate of spontaneous abortion.
- Infants born to drinking mothers have a high probability of being afflicted with fetal alcohol syndrome.

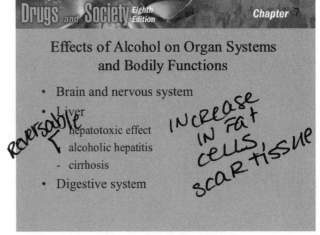

Effects of Alcohol on Organ Systems and Bodily Functions

- Brain and nervous system
- Liver
  - hepatotoxic effect
  - alcoholic hepatitis
  - cirrhosis
- Digestive system

Reversable *INCREASE IN FAT CELLS SCAR TISSUE*

Notes

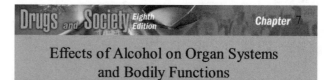

Effects of Alcohol on Organ Systems and Bodily Functions

- Blood
- Cardiovascular system
  - alcoholic cardiomyopathy
- Sexual organs
- Endocrine system

Effects of Alcohol on Organ Systems and Bodily Functions

- Kidneys
- Mental disorder and damage to the brain
  - Wernicke-korsakorr's syndrome
- The fetus (FAS)
- Malnutrition

Chapter 8: Alcohol: A Behavioral Perspective

Notes

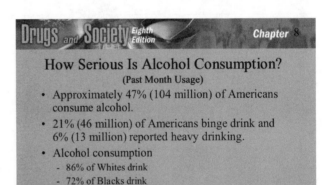

How Serious Is Alcohol Consumption?
(Past Month Usage)

- Approximately 47% (104 million) of Americans consume alcohol.
- 21% (46 million) of Americans binge drink and 6% (13 million) reported heavy drinking.
- Alcohol consumption
  - 86% of Whites drink
  - 72% of Blacks drink
  - 69% of Hispanics drink
- Estimated spending for health care services for alcohol problems and medical consequences of alcohol is $18.8 billion.

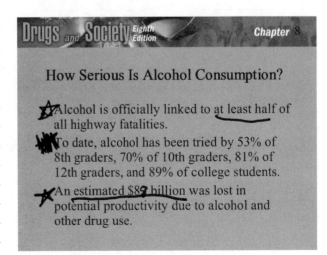

How Serious Is Alcohol Consumption?

- Alcohol is officially linked to at least half of all highway fatalities.
- To date, alcohol has been tried by 53% of 8th graders, 70% of 10th graders, 81% of 12th graders, and 89% of college students.
- An estimated $89 billion was lost in potential productivity due to alcohol and other drug use.

Notes

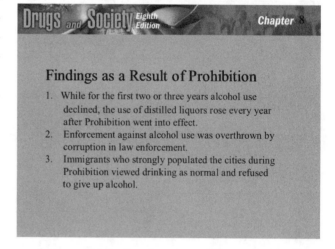

History of Alcohol (Ethanol) in America

- 1830 was the peak drinking period
- Prohibition period

Alcohol Has Coincided with Major Historical Events:

- Colonial America
- Triangle trade
- Colonial taverns (a key institution?)
- Temperance movement (1830–1850)
- Prohibition era (1920–1933)
  - Ratification of the Eighteenth Amendment (1919)
  - Alcohol was outlawed (January 1920)
    - Speakeasies
    - Bootlegging
    - Patent medicines
- In 1933 the 21st Amendment repealed prohibition

Findings as a Result of Prohibition

1. While for the first two or three years alcohol use declined, the use of distilled liquors rose every year after Prohibition went into effect.
2. Enforcement against alcohol use was overthrown by corruption in law enforcement.
3. Immigrants who strongly populated the cities during Prohibition viewed drinking as normal and refused to give up alcohol.

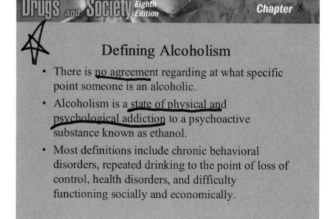

Defining Alcoholism

- There is no agreement regarding at what specific point someone is an alcoholic.
- Alcoholism is a state of physical and psychological addiction to a psychoactive substance known as ethanol.
- Most definitions include chronic behavioral disorders, repeated drinking to the point of loss of control, health disorders, and difficulty functioning socially and economically.

Defining Alcoholism (first definition)

World Health Organization (WHO) definition:

- *"Alcohol dependence syndrome* is characterized by a state, psychic and usually also physical, resulting from drinking alcohol. This state is characterized by behavioral and other responses that include a compulsion to take alcohol on a continuous or periodic basis to experience its psychic effects and sometimes to avoid the discomfort of its absence; tolerance may or may not be present" (NIAAA, 1980).

Drugs and Society *Eighth Edition* — Chapter 8

Defining Alcoholism (second definition)

- "Alcoholism is a chronic behavioral disorder manifested by repeated drinking of alcoholic beverages in excess of the dietary and social uses of the community, and to an extent that interferes with the drinker's health or his social or economic functioning" (Keller, 1958/78).

Drugs and Society *Eighth Edition* — Chapter 8

Defining Alcoholism (third definition)

- "Alcoholism is a chronic, primary, hereditary disease that progresses from an early, physiological susceptibility into an addiction characterized by tolerance changes, physiological dependence, and loss of control over drinking. Psychological symptoms are secondary to the physiological disease and not relevant to its onset" (Gold 1991, 99).

Drugs and **Society** *Eighth Edition* Chapter 8

Major Known Components of Alcoholism

–Craving
–Very impaired or loss of control
–Physical dependence
–Increasing tolerance

Drugs and **Society** *Eighth Edition* Chapter 8

Types of Alcoholics

- Alpha alcoholics
- Beta alcoholics
- Gamma alcoholics
- Delta alcoholics
- Epsilon alcoholics
- Zeta alcoholics

Drugs and **Society** *Eighth Edition* Chapter 8

Culture and Alcohol

- **Drunken comportment** is behavior exhibited while under the direct influence of alcohol determined by the norms and expectations of a particular culture.
- **Disinhibitor** is a psychoactive chemical that depresses thought and judgment functions in the cerebral cortex, which has the effect of allowing relatively unrestrained behavior (as in alcohol inebriation).

Drugs and **Society** *Eighth Edition*   **Chapter** 8

Culture and Alcohol

- Cultural rules state how much one can drink, and where.
- Cultures provide ceremonial meaning to alcohol use.
  - Drinking rates among Jews
  - Drinking rates among Irish
- Culture provides a model of alcoholism.
- Attitudes regarding drinking in the U.S.

Drugs and **Society** *Eighth Edition*   **Chapter** 8

Cultural Considerations

- Some psychologists contend that both *set and setting* can overshadow the pharmacological effects of most drugs, including alcohol.

  Set—an individual's expectation of what a drug will do to his/her personality

  Setting—the physical and social environment where most drugs, including alcohol, are consumed

---

Drugs and **Society** *Eighth Edition*   **Chapter** 8

Cultural Considerations

- Some sociologists contend that a culture's views and attitudes can influence effects of alcohol
  - Abstinent cultures (strictly prohibit alcohol)
  - Ambivalent cultures (contradictory views)
  - Permissive cultures (promote alcohol)
  - Over-permissive cultures (encourage alcohol)
- Which type or types of alcohol culture(s) does the U.S. have?

Drugs *and* **Society** *Eighth Edition* Chapter 8

Alcohol Abuse Among College and University Students

- CORE Institute research results:

  -- 300,000 of of the nation's 12 million college students will die of alcohol-related causes such as drunk-driving accidents, liver disorders, sexually transmitted diseases, cancers from alcohol abuse, and severely damaged organs from chronic drinking.

  -- College students consume an average of 4.3 drinks per week.

  Male students at smaller institutions consumed far more than those at larger institutions.

Drugs *and* **Society** *Eighth Edition* Chapter 8

Alcohol Abuse Among College and University Students (continued)

Other studies found that:

44% 42-50% of college students binge drink.

- Males binge drink more than females.
- For binge drinkers, the impact on impaired academic performance is just as great for women drinkers.
- Being white, involved in athletics, or a resident of a fraternity or sorority made it more likely that a student would be a binge drinker.

Drugs *and* **Society** *Eighth Edition* Chapter 8

Alcohol Abuse Among College and University Students (continued)

- On American campuses, alcohol is a factor in 40% of all academic problems and 28% of all dropouts.
- Seventy-five percent of male students and 55% of female students involved in acquaintance rape had been drinking or using drugs.
- The transition into college is associated with a doubling of the percentages of those who drink for both genders.
- With heavier drinkers, grades suffered for both male and female students.

Notes

Chapter 8

Women and Alcohol

- Women possess greater sensitivity to alcohol, have a greater likelihood of addiction, and develop alcohol-related health problems sooner than men.
- More women in alcohol treatment come from sexually abusive homes (70%), in comparison to men (12%).

Chapter 8

Three Major Reasons Why Women Are More Sensitive to the Effects of Alcohol

- Body Size (men generally larger than women)
- Women absorb alcohol sooner – women possess more body fat and body fat does not dilute alcohol
- Women possess less of a metabolizing enzyme – this enzyme gets rid of (processes out) alcohol

Chapter 8

Alcohol Consumption Patterns of Women

- Women 21 to 34 years of age were least likely to report alcohol-related problems if they had stable marriages and were working full time.
- Between 35 to 49 years of age, the heaviest drinkers were divorced or separated women without children.
- Between 50 to 64 years of age, the heaviest drinkers were women whose husbands/partners drank heavily.
- Women 65 and older comprised less than 10% of drinkers with drinking problems.

Notes

Alcohol is involved in 1/2 - 1/3 of highway fatalities

1/3 of traffic related injuries are alcohol related

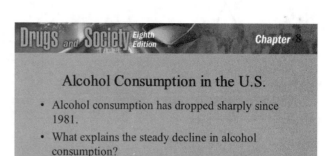

Alcohol Consumption in the U.S.

- Alcohol consumption has dropped sharply since 1981.
- What explains the steady decline in alcohol consumption?
  - Demographics
  - Conservatism
  - Decrease in social acceptability
  - Increase awareness of risks
  - Increase concerns for health

Additional Facts Regarding Alcohol Use/Abuse

- Drinking and Driving - On most weekend nights throughout the United States, 70% of all fatal single-vehicle crashes involve a driver who is legally intoxicated.
- Income/Wealth - Less affluent people drink less than more affluent individuals.
- The Average "Alcoholic" - Most alcoholics are secret or disguised drinkers who look very much like common working people.
- On Average - Most people who consume alcohol do not become problem drinkers

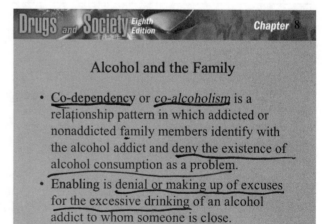

Alcohol and the Family

- Co-dependency or co-alcoholism is a relationship pattern in which addicted or nonaddicted family members identify with the alcohol addict and deny the existence of alcohol consumption as a problem.
- Enabling is denial or making up of excuses for the excessive drinking of an alcohol addict to whom someone is close.

Drugs *and* Society Eighth Edition Chapter 8

Alcohol and the Family (continued)

- Organizations for victims of alcoholics
  - Children of Alcoholics (COAs) 2–4 times more likely to become alcoholics themselves
  - Adult Children of Alcoholics (ACOAs) 2–4 times more likely to develop alcoholism
- It is estimated that there are 28.6 million COAs in the U.S. and 6.6 million are under the age of 18
- COAs and ACOAs are more likely to marry into families where alcoholism is prevalent
- 25% of American children are exposed to an alcoholic before the age of 18

Drugs *and* Society Eighth Edition Chapter 8

Helping the Family Recover

- **Psychodrama** is a family therapy in which significant inter- and intra-personal issues are enacted in a focused setting using dramatic techniques.
- **Genogram** is a family therapy technique that records information about behavior and relationships on a type of family tree to elucidate persistent patterns of dysfunctional behavior.
- **Role playing** is a therapeutic technique in which group members play assigned parts to elicit emotional actors.

Drugs *and* Society Eighth Edition Chapter 8

Helping the Family

- Post-traumatic stress disorder is a psychiatric syndrome in which an individual who has been exposed to a traumatic event or situation experiences psychological stress that may manifest itself in a wide range of symptoms, including re-experiencing the trauma, numbing of general responsiveness, and hyper-arousal.

Drugs and Society *Eighth Edition*   Chapter 8

Recovery from Alcoholism

- Treatment of alcoholism
  - Denial as a psychological defense
  - Easy to relapse without radical shift in lifestyle
  - Alcohol rehabilitation and medical ramifications
  - More emotionally fragile than other addicts
  - *Relapsing Syndrome*

NON USERS/
EARLY experimenters ——— PRIMARY & secondary experime-
PREVENTION-early nters
signs
of abuse

20-36% of suicides have history of alcohol abuse

40% of DROWNING is alcohol related

Drugs and Society *Eighth Edition*   Chapter 8

Withdrawal

- Relapsing Syndrome refers to returning to the use of alcohol after quitting.
- Acute alcohol withdrawal syndrome refers to symptoms that occur when an alcohol addicted individual does not maintain his/her usual blood alcohol level.
- Delirium tremens is the most severe, even life-threatening form of alcohol withdrawal, involving hallucinations, deliriums, and fever.

Notes

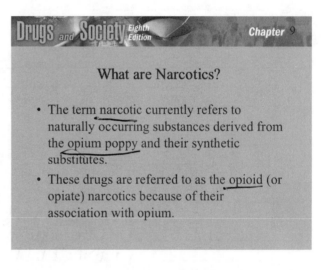

Notes

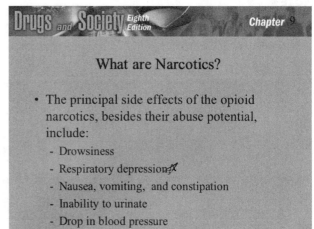

What are Narcotics?

- The principal side effects of the opioid narcotics, besides their abuse potential, include:
  - Drowsiness
  - Respiratory depression
  - Nausea, vomiting, and constipation
  - Inability to urinate
  - Drop in blood pressure

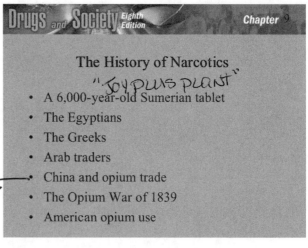

The History of Narcotics

"JOY PLUS PLANT"

- A 6,000-year-old Sumerian tablet
- The Egyptians
- The Greeks
- Arab traders
- China and opium trade ← OPIUM POPPY cause wide-spread addiction, banned it
- The Opium War of 1839
- American opium use

BRITION became angry
↓
OPIUM WAR
↓
LED TO LOSE OF HONG KONG (to G.B)

The History of Narcotics

BAYER
PHARMACEUTICAL PRODUCTS.
We are now sending to Physicians throughout the United States literature and samples of

ASPIRIN
The substitute for the Salicylates, agreeable of taste, free from unpleasant after-effects.

HEROIN ← 1803 ORIGINALLY COUGH SUPPRESSION
The Sedative for Coughs.
HEROIN HYDROCHLORIDE
Its water-soluble salt.
You will have call for them. Order a supply from your jobber.

Write for literature to
FARBENFABRIKEN OF ELBERFELD CO.
40 Stone Street, New York.

Pharmacological Effects

- The most common clinical use of the opioid narcotics is as analgesics to relieve pain.
- The opioid narcotics relieve pain by activating the same group of receptors that are controlled by the endogenous substances called endorphins.
- Activation of opioid receptors blocks the transmission of pain through the spinal cord or brain stem.

Drugs and Society, Eighth Edition — Chapter 9

Pharmacological Effects

- Morphine is a particularly potent pain reliever and often is used as the analgesic standard by which other narcotics are compared.
- With continual use, tolerance develops to the analgesic effects of morphine and other narcotics.
- Physicians frequently underprescribe narcotics, because of fear of causing narcotic addiction.

MIDTERM

Drugs and Society, Eighth Edition — Chapter 9

Abuse, Tolerance, Dependence, and Withdrawal

- All the opioid narcotic agents that activate opioid receptors have abuse potential and are classified as scheduled drugs.
- An estimated 0.6 million people in the U.S actively abuse heroin.
- Tolerance begins with the first dose of a narcotic, but does not become clinically evident until 2 to 3 weeks of frequent use.

Drugs and Society, Eighth Edition — Chapter 9

Notes

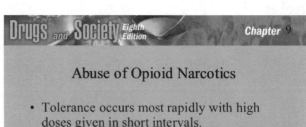

Abuse of Opioid Narcotics

- Tolerance occurs most rapidly with high doses given in short intervals.
- Doses can be increased as much as 35 times in order to regain the narcotic effect.
- Physical dependence invariably accompanies severe tolerance.
- Psychological dependence can also develop with continual narcotic use.

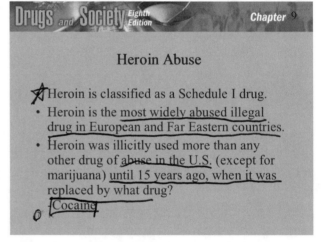

Heroin Abuse

- Heroin is classified as a Schedule I drug.
- Heroin is the most widely abused illegal drug in European and Far Eastern countries.
- Heroin was illicitly used more than any other drug of abuse in the U.S. (except for marijuana) until 15 years ago, when it was replaced by what drug?
  - Cocaine

called →
H, JUNK,
SMACK,
HORSE,
al capone,
bart simpson

Heroin Combinations

- Pure heroin is a white powder
- Heroin is usually "cut" (diluted) with lactose
- When heroin 1st enters the U.S., it may be 95% pure, by the time it is sold, it is 3 to 5% pure
- Heroin has a bitter taste and is often cut with quinine
- Heroin combined with cocaine is called "speedballing"

_____
_____
_____
_____
_____
_____
_____
_____
_____
_____
_____
_____

Drugs _and_ **Society** _Eighth Edition_   **Chapter** 9

Facts about Heroin Abuse

- Q. How many deaths occur annually in the United States from heroin overdoses?
- A. Approximately 3,000 to 4,000 deaths
- Q. What is the estimated number of heroin addicts in the United States?
- A. 500,000 to 750,000
- Q. What are "shooting galleries"?
- A. These locations serve as gathering places for addicts

_____
_____
_____

antisocial
personality

opium dens 1800s
safe alternative
to alcohol

_____
_____

Drugs _and_ **Society** _Eighth Edition_   **Chapter** 9

Heroin and Crime

- Factors related to crime:
  - Pharmacological effects encourage antisocial behavior that is crime related
  - Heroin diminishes inhibition
  - Addicts are self-centered, impulsive, and governed by need
  - Similar personality of criminal and addict
  - Cost of addiction

_____
_____
_____
_____
_____
_____
_____
_____
_____

Drugs _and_ **Society** _Eighth Edition_   **Chapter** 9

Patterns of Heroin Abuse

- Heroin use is holding steady
- Heroin has become purer (60 to 70% purity)
- Greater purity leads users to administer heroin in less efficient ways
- Many youths believe that heroin can be used safely if it is not injected

_____
_____

Notes

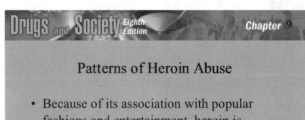

Patterns of Heroin Abuse

- Because of its association with popular fashions and entertainment, heroin is viewed as glamorous and chic, especially by many young people, despite its highly publicized lethal consequences.
- Emergency room visits due to narcotic overdoses increased significantly since 1990.

Stages of Dependence

- When narcotics such as heroin are first used by people not experiencing pain, the drugs can cause unpleasant, dysphoric sensations.
- Euphoria gradually overcomes the aversive effects.
- The positive feelings increase with narcotic use, leading to psychological dependence.

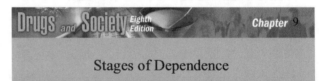

Stages of Dependence

- After psychological dependence, physical dependence occurs with frequent daily use, which reinforces narcotic abuse.
- If the user stops taking the drug after physical dependence has occurred severe withdrawal symptoms result.

Notes

SKIN POPPING-
INJECT UNDER SKIN

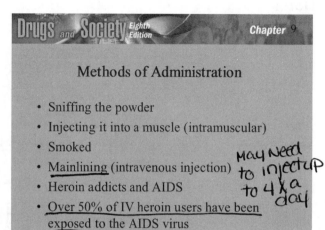

Methods of Administration

- Sniffing the powder
- Injecting it into a muscle (intramuscular)
- Smoked
- Mainlining (intravenous injection)
- Heroin addicts and AIDS
- Over 50% of IV heroin users have been exposed to the AIDS virus

May Need to inject up to 4 x a day

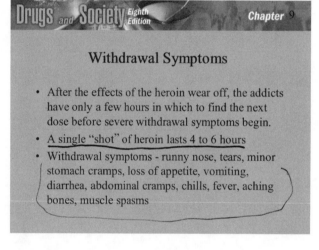

Withdrawal Symptoms

- After the effects of the heroin wear off, the addicts have only a few hours in which to find the next dose before severe withdrawal symptoms begin.
- A single "shot" of heroin lasts 4 to 6 hours
- Withdrawal symptoms - runny nose, tears, minor stomach cramps, loss of appetite, vomiting, diarrhea, abdominal cramps, chills, fever, aching bones, muscle spasms

Treatment

- Methadone, LAAM or buprenorphine are frequently used to help narcotic addicts
- Oral methadone relieves the withdrawal symptoms
- Methadone can cause psychological and physical dependence
- Buprenorphine was most recently approved by FDA for treating narcotic addiction

Notes

PATTERNS OF ABUSE

- USE - medical tx, escalate does by dr shopping

- USE - RECREATIONAL USE... done sporadically for months or yrs

✗✗✗✗ The younger an individual when drug use begins, more likely use will progress to dependence

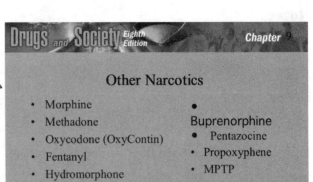

Other Narcotics

- Morphine
- Methadone
- Oxycodone (OxyContin)
- Fentanyl
- Hydromorphone
- Meperidine

-
- Buprenorphine
  - Pentazocine
- Propoxyphene
- MPTP
- Codeine

Narcotic-related Drugs

- Dextromethorphan (OTC antitussive)
- Clonidine (relieves some of the opioid withdrawal symptoms)
- Naloxone (opioid antagonist; used for narcotic overdoses)

Chapter 10: Stimulants

Notes

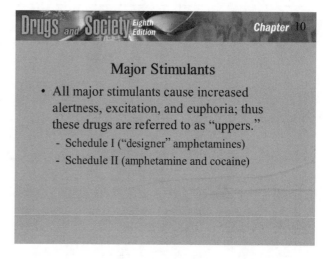

Major Stimulants

- All major stimulants cause increased alertness, excitation, and euphoria; thus these drugs are referred to as "uppers."
  - Schedule I ("designer" amphetamines)
  - Schedule II (amphetamine and cocaine)

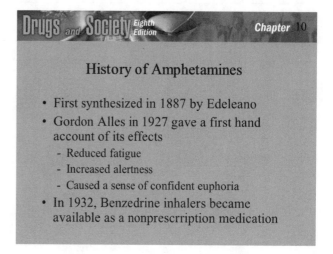

History of Amphetamines

- First synthesized in 1887 by Edeleano
- Gordon Alles in 1927 gave a first hand account of its effects
  - Reduced fatigue
  - Increased alertness
  - Caused a sense of confident euphoria
- In 1932, Benzedrine inhalers became available as a nonprescrription medication

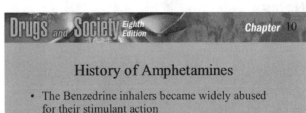

History of Amphetamines

- The Benzedrine inhalers became widely abused for their stimulant action
  - 1971, all potent amphetamine-like compounds in nasal inhalers were withdrawn from the market
- Widely used in World War II to counteract fatigue
- Other users: Korean War soldiers, college students, truck drivers, homemakers
- Air Force still gives pilots low doses of amphetamine to help them maintain alertness

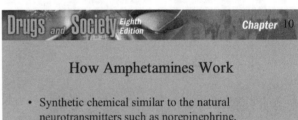

How Amphetamines Work

- Synthetic chemical similar to the natural neurotransmitters such as norepinephrine, dopamine, and epinephrine
- Exert their pharmacological effect by increasing the release and blocking the metabolism of these catecholamine substances as well as serotonin in the brain and from sympathetic nerves

How Amphetamines Work

- Causes alertness
- Can cause anxiety, severe apprehension, or panic
- Potent effects on dopamine in the reward center of the brain
- Behavioral stereotypy

Notes

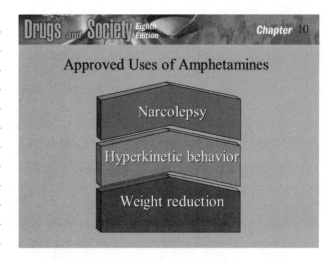

Approved Uses of Amphetamines

- Narcolepsy
- Hyperkinetic behavior
- Weight reduction

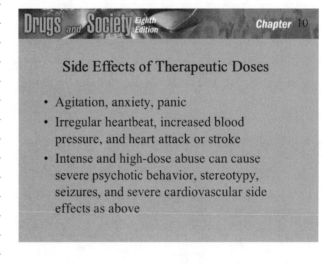

Side Effects of Therapeutic Doses

- Agitation, anxiety, panic
- Irregular heartbeat, increased blood pressure, and heart attack or stroke
- Intense and high-dose abuse can cause severe psychotic behavior, stereotypy, seizures, and severe cardiovascular side effects as above

Current Misuse

- Decline in abuse in the late '80s and early '90s
- In 1993 the declines were replaced by an alarming increase.
- Increase in use of methamphetamine led to the "National Methamphetamine Strategy" in 1996.
- Due to the ease of production, methamphetamine is often made in makeshift labs in homes or garages. Toxic chemicals and by products make these labs very dangerous.

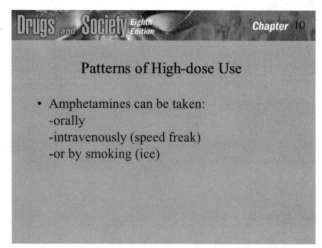

Patterns of High-dose Use

- Amphetamines can be taken:
  -orally
  -intravenously (speed freak)
  -or by smoking (ice)

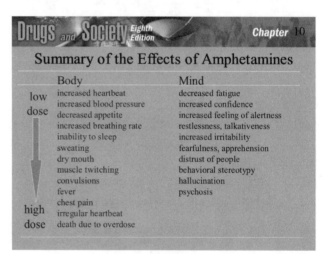

Summary of the Effects of Amphetamines

	Body	Mind
low dose	increased heartbeat	decreased fatigue
	increased blood pressure	increased confidence
	decreased appetite	increased feeling of alertness
	increased breathing rate	restlessness, talkativeness
	inability to sleep	increased irritability
	sweating	fearfulness, apprehension
	dry mouth	distrust of people
	muscle twitching	behavioral stereotypy
	convulsions	hallucination
	fever	psychosis
	chest pain	
high dose	irregular heartbeat	
	death due to overdose	

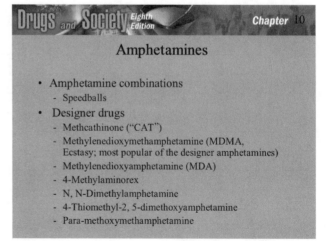

Amphetamines

- Amphetamine combinations
  - Speedballs
- Designer drugs
  - Methcathinone ("CAT")
  - Methylenedioxymethamphetamine (MDMA, Ecstasy; most popular of the designer amphetamines)
  - Methylenedioxyamphetamine (MDA)
  - 4-Methylaminorex
  - N, N-Dimethylamphetamine
  - 4-Thiomethyl-2, 5-dimethoxyamphetamine
  - Para-methoxymethamphetamine

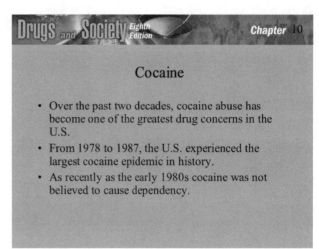

Cocaine

- Over the past two decades, cocaine abuse has become one of the greatest drug concerns in the U.S.
- From 1978 to 1987, the U.S. experienced the largest cocaine epidemic in history.
- As recently as the early 1980s cocaine was not believed to cause dependency.

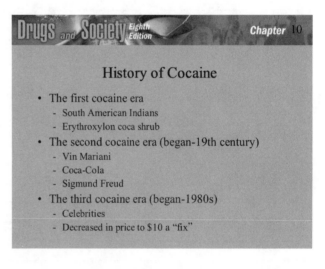

History of Cocaine

- The first cocaine era
  - South American Indians
  - Erythroxylon coca shrub
- The second cocaine era (began-19th century)
  - Vin Mariani
  - Coca-Cola
  - Sigmund Freud
- The third cocaine era (began-1980s)
  - Celebrities
  - Decreased in price to $10 a "fix"

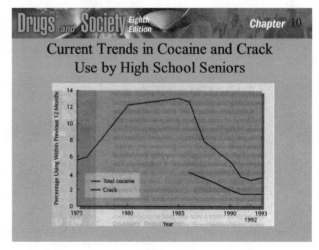

Current Trends in Cocaine and Crack Use by High School Seniors

Notes

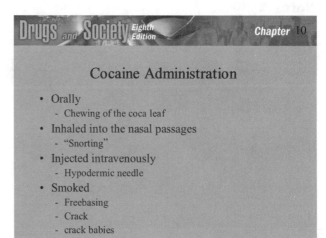

Cocaine Administration

- Orally
  - Chewing of the coca leaf
- Inhaled into the nasal passages
  - "Snorting"
- Injected intravenously
  - Hypodermic needle
- Smoked
  - Freebasing
  - Crack
  - crack babies

Pharmacological Effects of Cocaine

- Enhanced activity of the catecholamine and serotonin transmitters
- Blocks the reuptake of these substances following their release from neurons
- The summation of cocaine's effects on dopamine, noradrenaline, adrenaline, and serotonin is to cause CNS stimulation
  - Cardiovascular system
  - Local anesthetic effect

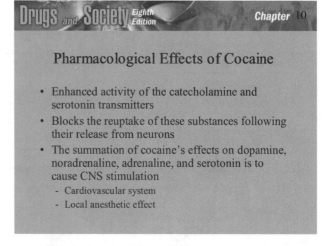

3 Main Stages of Cocaine Withdrawal

- The "crash" - the initial abstinence phase consisting of depression, agitation, suicidal thoughts, and fatigue
- Withdrawal - including mood swings, craving, anhedonia, and obsession with drug seeking
- Extinction - when normal pleasure returns, which cues trigger craving and mood swings

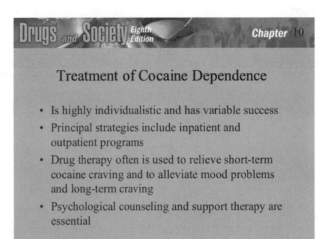

Treatment of Cocaine Dependence

- Is highly individualistic and has variable success
- Principal strategies include inpatient and outpatient programs
- Drug therapy often is used to relieve short-term cocaine craving and to alleviate mood problems and long-term craving
- Psychological counseling and support therapy are essential

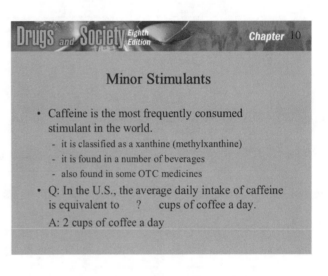

Minor Stimulants

- Caffeine is the most frequently consumed stimulant in the world.
  - it is classified as a xanthine (methylxanthine)
  - it is found in a number of beverages
  - also found in some OTC medicines
- Q: In the U.S., the average daily intake of caffeine is equivalent to ? cups of coffee a day.

  A: 2 cups of coffee a day

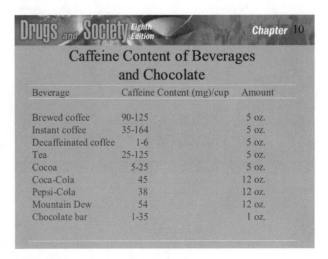

Caffeine Content of Beverages and Chocolate

Beverage	Caffeine Content (mg)/cup	Amount
Brewed coffee	90-125	5 oz.
Instant coffee	35-164	5 oz.
Decaffeinated coffee	1-6	5 oz.
Tea	25-125	5 oz.
Cocoa	5-25	5 oz.
Coca-Cola	45	12 oz.
Pepsi-Cola	38	12 oz.
Mountain Dew	54	12 oz.
Chocolate bar	1-35	1 oz.

Physiological Effects of Xanthines

- CNS effects
  - Enhances alertness, causes arousal, diminishes fatigue
- Adverse CNS effects
  - Insomnia, increase in tension, anxiety, and initiation of muscle twitches
  - Over 500 milligrams - panic sensations, chills, nausea, clumsiness
  - Extreme high doses (5 to 10 grams) - seizures, respiratory failure, and death

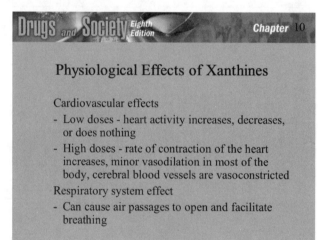

Physiological Effects of Xanthines

Cardiovascular effects
- Low doses - heart activity increases, decreases, or does nothing
- High doses - rate of contraction of the heart increases, minor vasodilation in most of the body, cerebral blood vessels are vasoconstricted

Respiratory system effect
- Can cause air passages to open and facilitate breathing

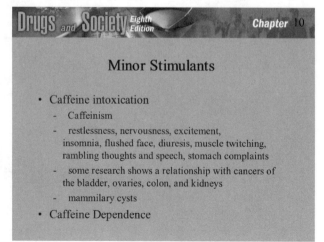

Minor Stimulants

- Caffeine intoxication
  - Caffeinism
  - restlessness, nervousness, excitement, insomnia, flushed face, diuresis, muscle twitching, rambling thoughts and speech, stomach complaints
  - some research shows a relationship with cancers of the bladder, ovaries, colon, and kidneys
  - mammilary cysts
- Caffeine Dependence

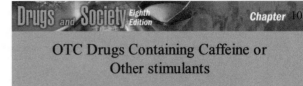

OTC Drugs Containing Caffeine or Other stimulants

- Analgesics
- Stay awake products
- Picker-uppers
- Decongestants
- Herbal Stimulants
  - Ephedrine (being abused by athletes, but prohibited by FDA)

Chapter 11: Tobacco

Notes

Tobacco Use:
Scope of the Problem

- Tobacco use is the leading preventable cause of disease and premature death in the U.S.
- 430,000 deaths annually in U.S.
- There are approximately 1.25 billion smokers in the world, and 800 million of these live in the developing world.

Current Tobacco Use

- In 2001, 66.5 million Americans smoked cigarettes
  - This represents 29.5 % among the U.S. population age 12 and older
- Males are more likely than females to report the use of any tobacco product

Notes

History of Tobacco Use

- Mayans: tobacco smoke as "divine incense"
- Turkey: poets vs. priests
- France: Louis XIII vs. Louis XIV
- Nicholas Monardes: infallible cure
- Pope Urban VII: excommunication for tobacco users

History in America

- Virginia and *Nicotiana tabacum*
- Chewing and snuffing predominated until the turn of the 20th century
- Flue-curing and puffing

Modern Government Regulation

- 1964—the Advisory Committee to the U.S. Surgeon General reported that cigarette smoking is related to lung cancer
- 1965—Congress passed legislation setting up the National Clearinghouse of Smoking and Health
- 1970—Warnings on cigarette labels

Master Settlement Agreement

• Involved 46 states and a $200 billion settlement

• Regulated outdoor advertisements, clothing, merchandise

• Established a trust fund to compensate tobacco farmers

Pharmacology of Nicotine

• It is a colorless, highly volatile liquid alkaloid.

• When smoked, nicotine enters the lungs and is then absorbed into the bloodstream.

• When chewed or dipped, nicotine is absorbed through the mucus lining of the mouth.

Pharmacology of Nicotine

• Amount of tobacco absorbed depends on:
  - Exact composition of tobacco
  - How densely the tobacco is packed
  - Whether a filter is used and characteristic of filter
  - The volume of smoke inhaled
  - The number of cigarettes smoked

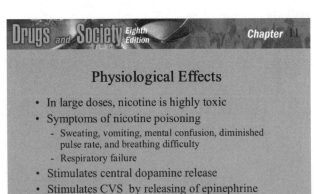

Physiological Effects

- In large doses, nicotine is highly toxic
- Symptoms of nicotine poisoning
  - Sweating, vomiting, mental confusion, diminished pulse rate, and breathing difficulty
  - Respiratory failure
- Stimulates central dopamine release
- Stimulates CVS by releasing of epinephrine
- Stimulates and then inhibit salivary and bronchial secretions

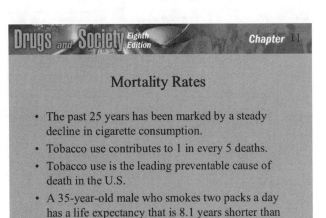

Mortality Rates

- The past 25 years has been marked by a steady decline in cigarette consumption.
- Tobacco use contributes to 1 in every 5 deaths.
- Tobacco use is the leading preventable cause of death in the U.S.
- A 35-year-old male who smokes two packs a day has a life expectancy that is 8.1 years shorter than his nonsmoking counterpart.

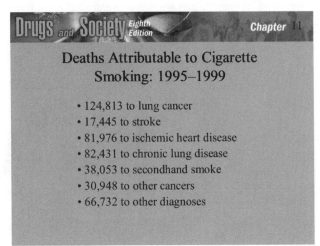

Deaths Attributable to Cigarette Smoking: 1995–1999

- 124,813 to lung cancer
- 17,445 to stroke
- 81,976 to ischemic heart disease
- 82,431 to chronic lung disease
- 38,053 to secondhand smoke
- 30,948 to other cancers
- 66,732 to other diagnoses

Chronic Illnesses and Smoking

- Men and women who smoke have more chronic illnesses, including:
  - Emphysema and bronchitis
  - Cardiovascular disease
  - Cancer
  - Bronchopulmonary disease
- Sudden infant death syndrome (SIDS)

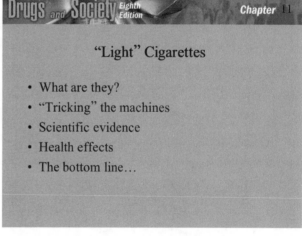

"Light" Cigarettes

- What are they?
- "Tricking" the machines
- Scientific evidence
- Health effects
- The bottom line…

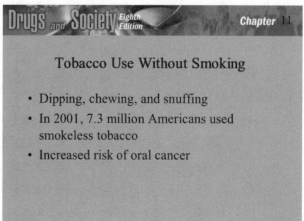

Tobacco Use Without Smoking

- Dipping, chewing, and snuffing
- In 2001, 7.3 million Americans used smokeless tobacco
- Increased risk of oral cancer

Secondhand and Sidestream Smoke

- Mainstream smoke—smoke drawn through the mouthpiece of the cigarette
- Sidestream smoke—smoke released into the air directly from the lighted tip of a cigarette
- Passive smoking—nonsmokers' inhalation of tobacco smoke
- Environmental tobacco smoke—sidestream smoke and exhaled mainstream smoke that is inhaled by the passive smoker

Who Smokes?

- 29.5% of population (66.5 million Americans) age 12 and older
- Males are more likely than females
- Current smokers are more likely to use alcohol or illicit drugs
- College graduates are the least likely to smoke

Methods for Quitting

- "Cold turkey"
- Behavioral modification
- Smoking cessation aids
  - Nicotine gum
  - Nicotine patches
  - Nicotine nasal spray
  - Nicotine inhalers
  - Bupropion

Notes

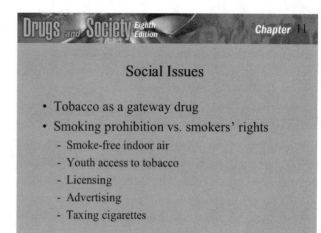

Social Issues

- Tobacco as a gateway drug
- Smoking prohibition vs. smokers' rights
  - Smoke-free indoor air
  - Youth access to tobacco
  - Licensing
  - Advertising
  - Taxing cigarettes

Chapter 12: Hallucinogens (Psychedelics)

Notes

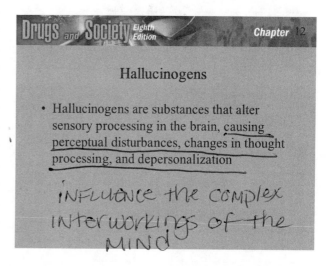

Hallucinogens

- Hallucinogens are substances that alter sensory processing in the brain, causing perceptual disturbances, changes in thought processing, and depersonalization

outside of yourself

iNFLUENCE the COMPLEX iNTERWORKINGS of the MIND

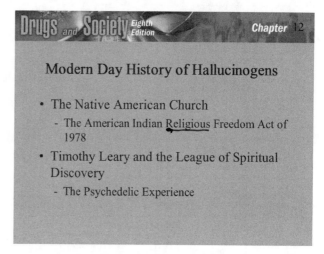

Modern Day History of Hallucinogens

- The Native American Church
  - The American Indian Religious Freedom Act of 1978
- Timothy Leary and the League of Spiritual Discovery
  - The Psychedelic Experience

Drugs and **Society** *Eighth Edition*   *Chapter* 12

The Nature of Hallucinogens

- Many drugs can exert hallucinogenic effects
  - LSD types
  - Phenylethylamines
  - Anticholinergic agents

Drugs and **Society** *Eighth Edition*   *Chapter* 12

Nature of Hallucinogens

type of mind altering experience

Psychedelic

Psychotogenic

Psychotomimetic

Drugs and **Society** *Eighth Edition*   *Chapter* 12

Sensory and Psychological Effects of Hallucinogens

- Altered senses   *can see sound, hear colors*
  - synesthesia
- Loss of control
  - flashbacks
- Self-reflection
  - "make conscious the unconscious"
- Loss of identity and cosmic merging
  - "mystical-spiritual aspect of the drug experience"

Notes

Traditional Hallucinogens:
LSD Types of Agents

- LSD (lysergic acid diethylamide), mescaline, psilocybin, dimethyltryptamine (DMT), and myristicin
- These drugs cause predominantly psychedilic effects
- Of high school seniors sampled:
  - 1999 – 12.2% had used LSD sometime during life
  - 2002 – 8.4% had used LSD sometime during life

Traditional Hallucinogens:
LSD Types of Agents

- Physical properties of LSD
  - In pure form - colorless, odorless, tasteless
  - Street names - acid, blotter acid, microdot, white lightning
- Physiological effects
  - Massive increase in neural activity in some brain regions
  - Activates sympathetic nervous system (rise in body temp., heart rate, and blood pressure)
  - Parasympathetic nervous system (increase in salivation and nausea)

Traditional Hallucinogens:
LSD Types of Agents

- About half of the substance is cleared from the body within 3 hours, and more than 90% is excreted within 24 hours
- Effects of of this hallucinogen can last 2-12 hours
- Tolerance to the effects of LSD develops very quickly

FOUR GROUPS

1 Traditional (LSD)
2 DOP, MDA, MDMA
3
4

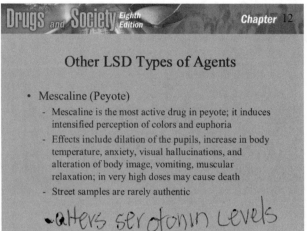

Drugs and Society Eighth Edition — Chapter 12

Other LSD Types of Agents

- Mescaline (Peyote)
  - Mescaline is the most active drug in peyote; it induces intensified perception of colors and euphoria
  - Effects include dilation of the pupils, increase in body temperature, anxiety, visual hallucinations, and alteration of body image, vomiting, muscular relaxation; in very high doses may cause death
  - Street samples are rarely authentic

- alters serotonin levels

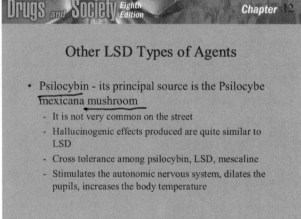

Drugs and Society Eighth Edition — Chapter 12

Other LSD Types of Agents

- Psilocybin - its principal source is the Psilocybe mexicana mushroom
  - It is not very common on the street
  - Hallucinogenic effects produced are quite similar to LSD
  - Cross tolerance among psilocybin, LSD, mescaline
  - Stimulates the autonomic nervous system, dilates the pupils, increases the body temperature

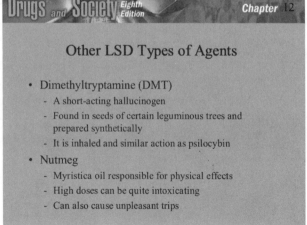

Drugs and Society Eighth Edition — Chapter 12

Other LSD Types of Agents

- Dimethyltryptamine (DMT)
  - A short-acting hallucinogen
  - Found in seeds of certain leguminous trees and prepared synthetically
  - It is inhaled and similar action as psilocybin
- Nutmeg
  - Myristica oil responsible for physical effects
  - High doses can be quite intoxicating
  - Can also cause unpleasant trips

Notes

Phenylethylamine Hallucinogens

- The phenylethylamine drugs are chemically related to amphetamines.
- They have varying degrees of hallucinogenic and CNS stimulant effects
- Phenylethylamines that predominantly:
  - Release serotonin are dominated by their hallucinogenic action
  - Release dopamine are dominated by their stimulant effects

Phenylethylamine Hallucinogens

- Dimthoxymethylamphetamine (DOM or STP)
- "Designer" amphetamines
- 3,4-Methylenedioxyamphetamine (MDA)
- Methylenedioxymethamphetamine (MDMA, Ecstasy)

Anticholinergic Hallucinogens

- The anticholinergic hallucinogens include naturally occurring alkaloid substances that are present in plants and herbs
- The potato family of plants contains most of these mind-altering drugs
- 3 potent anticholinergic compounds
  - Scopolamine
  - Hyoscyamine
  - Atropine

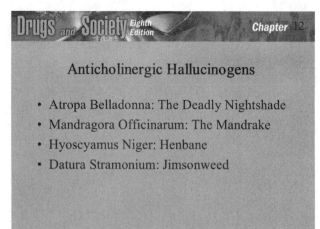

Drugs *and* **Society** *Eighth Edition* — *Chapter* 12

Anticholinergic Hallucinogens

- Atropa Belladonna: The Deadly Nightshade
- Mandragora Officinarum: The Mandrake
- Hyoscyamus Niger: Henbane
- Datura Stramonium: Jimsonweed

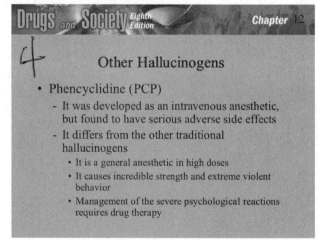

Drugs *and* **Society** *Eighth Edition* — *Chapter* 12

Other Hallucinogens

- Phencyclidine (PCP)
  - It was developed as an intravenous anesthetic, but found to have serious adverse side effects
  - It differs from the other traditional hallucinogens
    - It is a general anesthetic in high doses
    - It causes incredible strength and extreme violent behavior
    - Management of the severe psychological reactions requires drug therapy

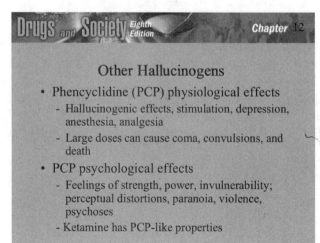

Drugs *and* **Society** *Eighth Edition* — *Chapter* 12

Other Hallucinogens

- Phencyclidine (PCP) physiological effects
  - Hallucinogenic effects, stimulation, depression, anesthesia, analgesia
  - Large doses can cause coma, convulsions, and death
- PCP psychological effects
  - Feelings of strength, power, invulnerability; perceptual distortions, paranoia, violence, psychoses
  - Ketamine has PCP-like properties

Chapter 13: Marijuana

Notes

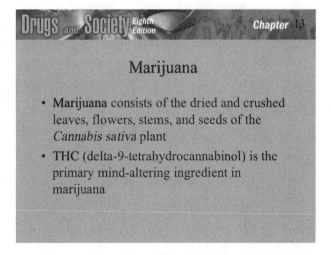

Marijuana

- **Marijuana** consists of the dried and crushed leaves, flowers, stems, and seeds of the *Cannabis sativa* plant
- THC (delta-9-tetrahydrocannabinol) is the primary mind-altering ingredient in marijuana

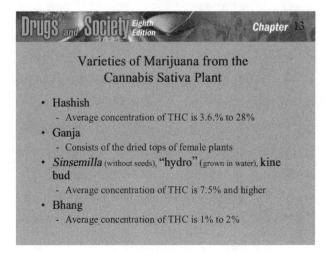

Varieties of Marijuana from the Cannabis Sativa Plant

- Hashish
  - Average concentration of THC is 3.6.% to 28%
- Ganja
  - Consists of the dried tops of female plants
- *Sinsemilla* (without seeds), "hydro" (grown in water), kine bud
  - Average concentration of THC is 7.5% and higher
- Bhang
  - Average concentration of THC is 1% to 2%

Notes

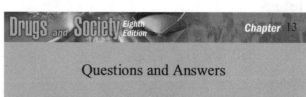

Questions and Answers

Q: Today marijuana is how many times more potent than the marijuana on the street in the 1960s and 1970s?

A: Approximately 20 times more potent

Q: How many Americans are current marijuana users?

A: Aged 12 or older in 2001: Out of 15.9 million illicit drug users, 56% (8.9 million) reported using only marijuana, 24% (3.8 million) used an illicit drug but not marijuana, and 20% (3.1 million) used marijuana and some other drug

Some Noteworthy Findings Regarding Marijuana Users

- The highest rate of use was found among young adults (ages 18-25) with 18.8% reporting current use and among youth (ages 12-17) with 10.8% use.

- The average age of first use was 17.5 years.

- There were 2.4 million new marijuana users in 2000.

Influencing Factors

- **Structural factors**
  - Age, gender, family background, religious beliefs (or lack of)
- **Social and interactional factors**
  - Type of interpersonal relationships, friendship cliques, drug use within the peer group setting
- **Setting**
  - Type of community and neighborhood (physical location of drug use)
- **Attitudinal factors**
  - Personal attitudes toward the use of drugs, self esteem, maturation level, etc.

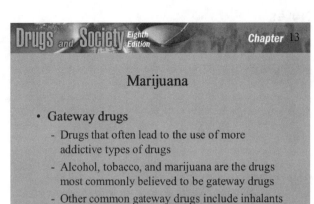

Marijuana

- Gateway drugs
  - Drugs that often lead to the use of more addictive types of drugs
  - Alcohol, tobacco, and marijuana are the drugs most commonly believed to be gateway drugs
  - Other common gateway drugs include inhalants and anabolic steroids.

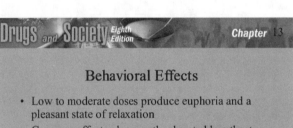

Behavioral Effects

- Low to moderate doses produce euphoria and a pleasant state of relaxation
- Common effects: dry mouth, elevated heartbeat, some loss of coordination and balance, slower reaction times, reddening of the eyes, elevated blood pressure, some mental confusion (short-term memory loss)
- A typical high lasts from 2–3 hours, and the user experiences altered perception of space and time as well as impaired memory

Behavioral Effects

- An acute dose of cannabis can produce adverse reactions: mild anxiety to panic and paranoia
- In a minority of cases users can exhibit psychoses, delusional and bizarre behavior, and hallucinations. These reactions occur most frequently in individuals who are under stress, anxious, depressed, or borderline schizophrenic and are using the more potent types of marijuana.

Notes

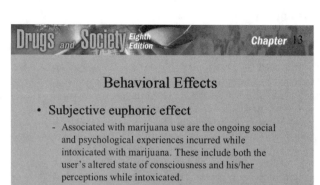

Behavioral Effects

- Subjective euphoric effect
  - Associated with marijuana use are the ongoing social and psychological experiences incurred while intoxicated with marijuana. These include both the user's altered state of consciousness and his/her perceptions while intoxicated.
  - Differential association
    - Behavioral satisfaction derived from friends who use marijuana ("fun-times when high with friends")

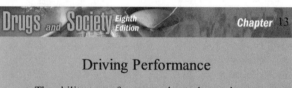

Driving Performance

- The ability to perform complex tasks, such as driving, is often impaired while under the influence of marijuana.
- In limited surveys, from 60% to 80% of marijuana users indicate that they sometimes drive while being high.
- A 1998 study found that of 1800 blood samples taken from drivers arrested for driving while intoxicated, 19% tested positive for marijuana.

Critical Thinking Skills

- Marijuana has been found to have a negative impact on critical thinking skills
- Alertness, memory, and learning are impaired under the use of marijuana
- The unresolved question is whether these impairments are short term or long term

Notes

Drugs and Society Eighth Edition — Chapter 13

Amotivational Syndrome

- **Amotivational Syndrome** characterizes regular users of marijuana who experience a lack of motivation and reduced productivity
- Specifically, users show apathy, a poor short-term memory, difficulty with concentration, and a lingering disinterest in pursuing goals

Drugs and Society Eighth Edition — Chapter 13

Physiological Effects

- Central Nervous System (coordination)
- Respiratory System
- Cardiovascular System (binds hemoglobin-limiting oxygen to heart, increase in heart rate)
- Sexual Performance and Reproduction (aphrodisiac; sterility, impotence, depression of sex drive, lowers sperm cell counts; sympathetic NS)

Drugs and Society Eighth Edition — Chapter 13

Effects of Marijuana on the Central Nervous System

- Altered perceptions
  - Changes in the interpretation of stimuli resulting from marijuana use
- "Munchies"
  - Hunger experienced while under the effects of marijuana
- Anandamide
  - Possible neurotransmitter acting at the marijuana (cannabinoid) receptor

Notes

Therapeutic Uses of Marijuana

Medical marijuana use - Involves using the THC derived from smoking marijuana or using Marinol,* in cannabis as a drug to calm or relieve symptoms of an illness

Some Research shows that THC can be used for treating:

- Glaucoma
  - Potentially blinding eye disease causing continual and increasing intraocular pressure

*Marinol is an FDA-approved THC in capsule form (dronabinol)

Therapeutic Uses of Marijuana (continued)

- Appetite stimulant – patients experiencing anorexia, AIDS, chemotherapy and radiation therapy
- Antiseizure – aids in the prevention of seizures (epilepsy)
- Muscle relaxation – aids in muscle spasms
- Analgesic effect – in patients experiencing frequent migraines and chronic headaches or inflammation

Arguments Against Marijuana Use

- It contains 421 chemicals
- It is stronger than it was 20 years ago
- It is far worse for the lungs than tobacco
- It causes "amotivational syndrome"
- It is illegal and has no medical use whatsoever (NORML 2000)

Drugs and Society Eighth Edition   Chapter 13

Effects on Other Systems

- Alveolar Macrophages (Respiratory System)
  - Special white blood cells that play a role in cleaning lung tissue are less able to remove debris when exposed to smoke
- Vasodilation (Cardiovascular System)
  - Enlarged blood vessels (blood shot eyes)
- Aphrodisiac (Sexual Performance and Reproduction)
  - Refers to a compound that is believed to cause sexual arousal

Drugs and Society Eighth Edition   Chapter 13

DSM-IV Regarding Cannabis Dependence

- Cannabis dependence is characterized by "compulsive use" in acquiring and spending hours per day using the substance. These users persist in their use despite knowledge of physical problems (for example, chronic cough related to smoking) or psychological problems (for example, excessive sedation resulting from repeated use of high doses; APA 1994)

Chapter 14: Inhalants

Notes

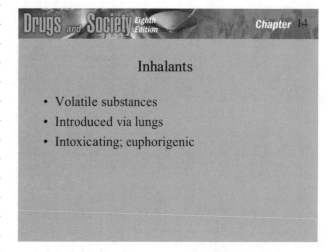

Inhalants

- Volatile substances
- Introduced via lungs
- Intoxicating; euphorigenic

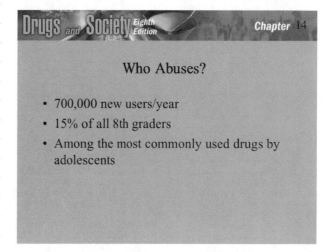

Who Abuses?

- 700,000 new users/year
- 15% of all 8th graders
- Among the most commonly used drugs by adolescents

Notes

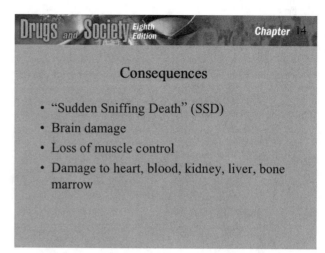

Consequences

- "Sudden Sniffing Death" (SSD)
- Brain damage
- Loss of muscle control
- Damage to heart, blood, kidney, liver, bone marrow

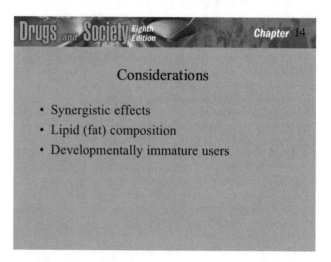

Considerations

- Synergistic effects
- Lipid (fat) composition
- Developmentally immature users

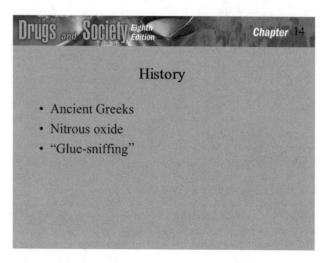

History

- Ancient Greeks
- Nitrous oxide
- "Glue-sniffing"

Notes

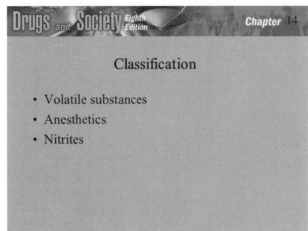

Classification

- Volatile substances
- Anesthetics
- Nitrites

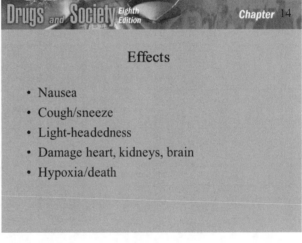

Effects

- Nausea
- Cough/sneeze
- Light-headedness
- Damage heart, kidneys, brain
- Hypoxia/death

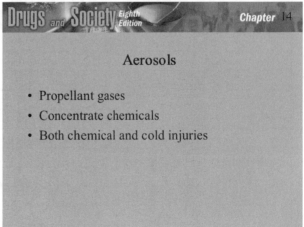

Aerosols

- Propellant gases
- Concentrate chemicals
- Both chemical and cold injuries

Notes

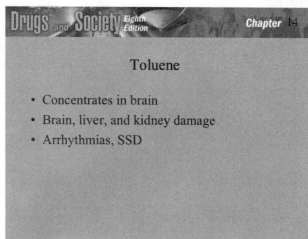

Toluene

- Concentrates in brain
- Brain, liver, and kidney damage
- Arrhythmias, SSD

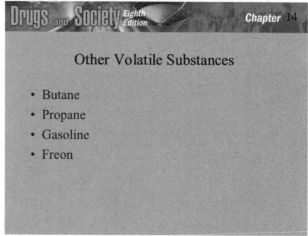

Other Volatile Substances

- Butane
- Propane
- Gasoline
- Freon

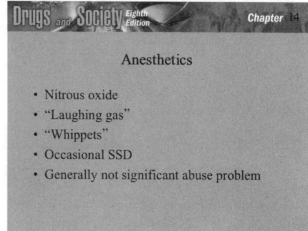

Anesthetics

- Nitrous oxide
- "Laughing gas"
- "Whippets"
- Occasional SSD
- Generally not significant abuse problem

Notes

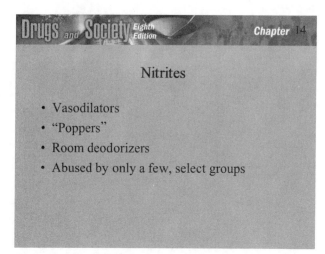

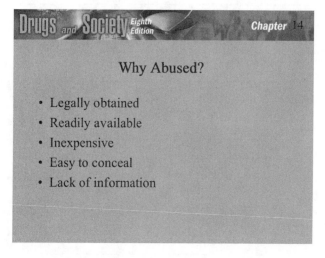

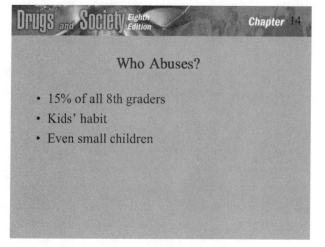

New Trends

- Schoolchildren's perceptions are changing
- Perception of risk has increased, and use is beginning to trend downward

Who Abuses?

- More men than women (for now...)
- Often poor self-image, difficult environment (but not always...)
- Episodic outbreaks

Signs of Abuse

- Appear drunken
- Red, watery eyes
- "Sniffles" without other signs of cold
- Slurred speech
- Rashes on nose and mouth

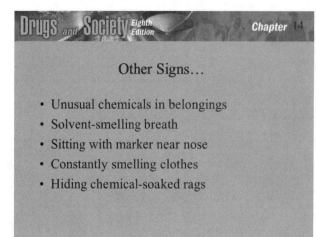

Other Signs…

- Unusual chemicals in belongings
- Solvent-smelling breath
- Sitting with marker near nose
- Constantly smelling clothes
- Hiding chemical-soaked rags

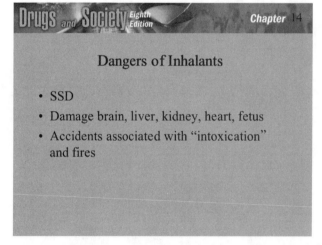

Dangers of Inhalants

- SSD
- Damage brain, liver, kidney, heart, fetus
- Accidents associated with "intoxication" and fires

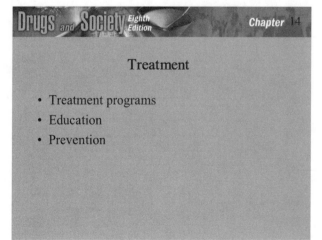

Treatment

- Treatment programs
- Education
- Prevention

Chapter 15: Over-the-Counter (OTC), Prescription, and Herbal Drugs

Notes

Prescription & OTC Drugs

- Prescription drugs are available only by recommendation of an authorized health professional, such as a physician.
- Nonprescription (over-the-counter, or OTC) drugs are available on request and do not require approval by a health professional.

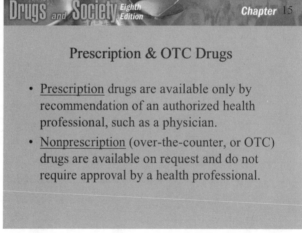

Prescription & OTC Drugs

- Prescription and OTC drugs have been viewed differently by the public since the classifications were established by the Durham-Humphrey Amendment of 1951.
- In general, the public views OTC drugs as minimally effective and safe and prescription drugs as more potent and frequently dangerous
- However, these distinctions are not always accurate

Notes

OTC Drugs Interesting Facts

- Each year the U.S. spends over $14 billion on OTC drugs
- More than 300,000 different OTC products are available on the market
- OTC expenditures comprise 60% of the annual drug purchase in the U.S.
- An estimated 3 out of 4 people routinely self-medicate with these drug products

Abuse of OTC Products

- OTC products generally have a greater margin of safety than their prescription counterparts, but issues of abuse need to be considered.
- Physical dependence
- Psychological dependence

Abuse of OTC Products

- Nonprescription products that can be severely habit-forming: decongestants, laxatives, antihistamines, sleep aids, and antacids.
- The active ingredients in OTC drugs have been classified and placed in category I (considered safe and effective)

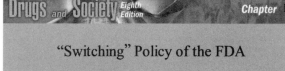

"Switching" Policy of the FDA

- The FDA is attempting to make more drugs available to the general public by switching some frequently used and safe prescription medications to OTC status.

- This policy is in response to public demand to have access to effective drugs for self-medication and has resulted in approximately 700 drug products switching from prescription to OTC status

OTC Drugs and Self-care

- The majority of health problems treated in the United States can be treated with OTC medications.

- If done correctly, self-care with OTC medications can provide significant relief from minor, self-limiting health problems at minimal cost.

OTC Labels

- Required label information includes:
  - Approved uses of the product
  - Detailed instructions on safe and effective use
  - Cautions or warnings to those at greatest risk when taking the medication

Notes

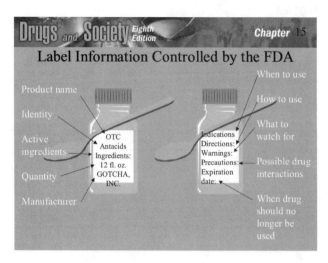

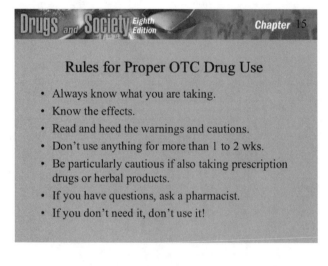

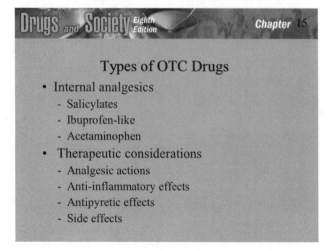

Types of OTC Drugs

- Cold, allergy and cough remedies
  - Decongestants
  - Antitussives
  - Expectorants
  - Vitamin C
- Sleep aids
  - Antihistamines
  - Melatonin
- Stimulants
  - Stay-awake or energy-promoting

Types of OTC Drugs

- Gastrointestinal medication
  - Antacids and anti-heartburn medication
- Diet aids
- Skin products
  - Acne medications
  - Sun products
- Skin first-aid products
- OTC herbal products

Prescription Drugs

- There are currently more than 10,000 prescription products sold in the United States, representing:
  - Approximately 1500 different drugs
  - With 20 to 50 new medications approved each year by the FDA

Prescription Drugs

- According to the Durham-Humphrey Amendment of 1951, drugs are controlled with prescription if they are:
  - Habit-forming
  - Not safe for self-medication
  - Intended to treat ailments that require the supervisions of a health professional
  - New and without an established safe track record

Doctor-patient Communication

- When a physician prescribes a drug, a patient should insist on answers to the following questions:
  -What is the desired outcome?
  -What are the possible side effects of the drug?
  -How should the drug be taken to minimize problems and maximize benefits?

Generic and Proprietary Drugs

- Generic is the official, nonpatented, nonproprietary name of a drug. The term generic is used by the public to refer to the common name of a drug that is not subject to trademark rights.
- Proprietary, a brand or trademark name that is registered with the U.S. Patent Office. Proprietary denoted medications are marketed under specific brand names, i.e., Valium.

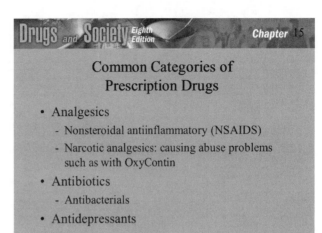

Common Categories of
Prescription Drugs

- Analgesics
  - Nonsteroidal antiinflammatory (NSAIDS)
  - Narcotic analgesics: causing abuse problems
    such as with OxyContin
- Antibiotics
  - Antibacterials
- Antidepressants

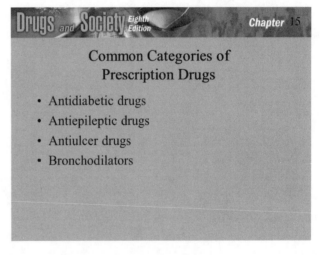

Common Categories of
Prescription Drugs

- Antidiabetic drugs
- Antiepileptic drugs
- Antiulcer drugs
- Bronchodilators

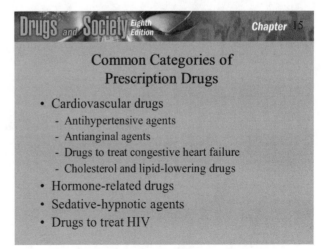

Common Categories of
Prescription Drugs

- Cardiovascular drugs
  - Antihypertensive agents
  - Antianginal agents
  - Drugs to treat congestive heart failure
  - Cholesterol and lipid-lowering drugs
- Hormone-related drugs
- Sedative-hypnotic agents
- Drugs to treat HIV

Chapter 16: Drug Use Within Major Subcultures

Notes

_____

_____

_____

_____

_____

_____

_____

_____

_____

_____

_____

_____

_____

_____

_____

_____

_____

_____

_____

_____

_____

_____

_____

_____

_____

_____

_____

_____

_____

_____

_____

_____

_____

_____

_____

_____

_____

_____

_____

_____

_____

_____

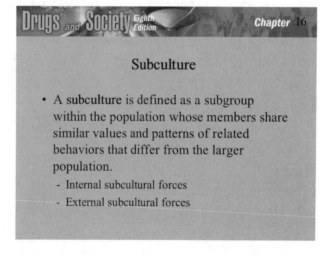

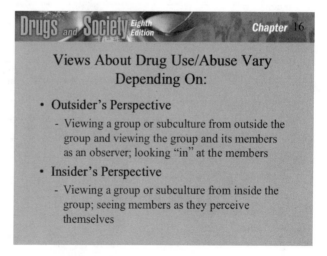

Notes

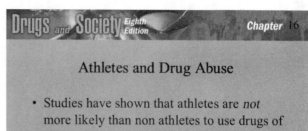

Athletes and Drug Abuse

- Studies have shown that athletes are *not* more likely than non athletes to use drugs of abuse such as marijuana, alcohol, barbiturates, cocaine, and hallucinogens. However, athletes are much more likely than other populations to take drugs (ergogenic drugs) to enhance performance.

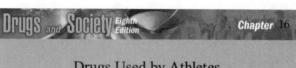

Drugs Used by Athletes

- Anabolic steroids consist of a group of natural and synthetic drugs that are chemically similar to cholesterol and related to the male hormone testosterone.
- Naturally occurring male hormones, or **androgens** are produced by the testes in males.

Abuse of Anabolic Steroids by Athletes

- Under some conditions, androgen-like drugs can increase muscle mass and strength
- It is estimated that as many as 1 million Americans have used or are currently using these drugs to achieve a "competitive edge"
- Two percent of college-age men
- 6.7% of male high school athletes
- 1% of female high school athletes

Drugs *and* Society *Eighth Edition* Chapter 16

Steroid Use by Children and Adolescents

- 52,000 American children and adolescents are using anabolic steroids.
- One study in the journal *Pediatrics* found that in Massachusetts middle schools, 2.7% of athletes were using steroids (Begley et al. 1999, p.54).
- Another source found that males are much more likely to use and abuse steroids than females (NIDA, 2001).

Drugs *and* Society *Eighth Edition* Chapter 16

Patterns of Anabolic Steroid Use by Athletes
Can you define each of these terms?

- Stacking
- Cycling
- Plateauing
- Pyramiding
- Array

Drugs *and* Society *Eighth Edition* Chapter 16

Effects of Anabolic Steroids

- Increase strength
- Gain in lean body mass
- Increase "bad" blood cholesterol
- Increased risk of liver disorders
- Psychological effects (irritability, outbursts of anger—"roid rage," mania, psychosis, and major depression)
- Psychological and physical dependence with continual use of high doses

Notes

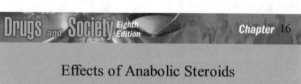

Effects of Anabolic Steroids

- Withdrawal symptoms—craving, fatigue, depression, restlessness, loss of appetite, insomnia, diminished sex drive, headaches
- Alterations in reproductive systems and sex hormones (breast enlargement in males, breast reduction and hair growth in females, infertility, and atrophy—shrinkage of penis and testicles in males and enlargement of external genitalia in females)

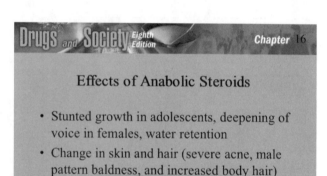

Effects of Anabolic Steroids

- Stunted growth in adolescents, deepening of voice in females, water retention
- Change in skin and hair (severe acne, male pattern baldness, and increased body hair)
- Persistent unpleasant breath odor
- Swelling of feet and limbs

Drugs Used by Athletes

- Stimulants (amphetamines and cocaine)
- Clenbuterol
- Erythropoietin
- Human growth factor (HGF) and human growth hormone (HGH)
- ß (Beta)-adrenergic blockers
- Gamma-hydroxybutyrate

Drugs and **Society** *Eighth Edition*   *Chapter* 16

Drug Use Among Women

- Overall, females consistently use fewer licit and illicit drugs (24% of females versus 31% of males use illicit drugs).
- More males (29%) than females (22%) use marijuana on a yearly basis.
- Males (84%) and females (83%) are nearly equal with regard to the consumption of alcohol. However, with regard to binge drinking greater differences exist between males (43%) than females (24%).
- Females (2.7%) are less likely to use hallucinogen-type drugs than males (6.5%).
- Steroid use among young adults is much more prevalent among males than females

Drugs and **Society** *Eighth Edition*   *Chapter* 16

Q. How do the following drugs affect a Woman's Reproduction?

- Cocaine?
- Alcohol?
- Tobacco?
- Other drugs (marijuana, LSD, other depressant drugs)?

Drugs and **Society** *Eighth Edition*   *Chapter* 16

Women and Alcohol

- Alcohol is the drug most widely used and abused by women in the U.S.
  - Women aged 12 and older - 42.3% used alcohol in the past month and 19.4 reported binge drinking (SAMHSA 1999)
- Unlike men, women are less likely to develop severe alcohol dependence (only 25% of the alcoholics in the U.S. are female)
- Women dependent on alcohol are judged more harshly than men dependent on alcohol

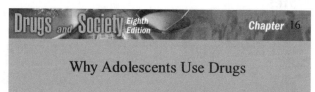

Why Adolescents Use Drugs

- Most adolescents who use substances of abuse do so with normal psychosocial development and will not develop problematic dependence on these drugs.
- The adolescent users who have difficulty with drugs often lack coping skills, have dysfunctional families, poor self images, and/or feel socially and emotionally insecure.

Why Adolescents Use Drugs (continued)

- Parents who are most likely to foster drug abusing children are:
  - Drug abusers themselves
  - Excessively rigid and condemning
  - Overly demanding
  - Overly protective
  - Overwhelmed with their own personal conflicts
  - Unable to effectively communicate with their children

Why Adolescents Use Drugs (continued)

- Recent research indicates that the most important factor influencing drug use among adolescents is peer drug use.
- Research also shows that there exists a correlation between strong family bonds and non drug-using peer groups.
- Use drugs to cope with boredom, unpleasant feelings, emotions, and stress or to relieve depression, reduce tension, and reduce alienation.
- What other explanations can you offer that may explain why adolescents use drugs?

Notes

Drugs and Society *Eighth Edition*

Patterns of Drug Use in Adolescents

- Fill in the blanks regarding recent surveys on lifetime drug patterns of 8th graders in 1999.
  A.___% had used alcohol
  B.___% had used cigarettes
  C.___% had used inhalants
  D.___% had used marijuana

Key: A is 52%, B is 44%, C is 20%, and D is 22%

Drugs and Society *Eighth Edition* — Chapter 16

Patterns of Drug Use in Adolescents

- Fill in the blanks regarding recent surveys (2000) on lifetime drug patterns of 12th graders.
  A.___% had used alcohol
  B.___% had used cigarettes
  C.___% had used inhalants
  D.___% had used marijuana

Key: A is 80%, B is 63%, C is 14%, and D is 49%.

Drugs and Society *Eighth Edition* — Chapter 16

Consequences of Adolescent Drug Use

- Adolescent suicide
- Sexual violence and drugs
- Gangs and drugs

Drugs and Society Eighth Edition — Chapter 16

Prevention and Treatment of Adolescent Drug Problems

- Encourage parental awareness of gangs
- Encourage alternative participation in organizations or groups (athletics, school activities, career development, or involvement volunteering programs)
- Help children to develop coping skills regarding frustration and stress
- Educate children about gang-related problems and help them understand that like drugs, gangs are the result of problems and are not the solutions to problems

Drugs and Society Eighth Edition — Chapter 16

Major Reasons Cited by College Students for Their Drug Use*

- To have fun (78.9%)
- To relieve stress (63.9%)
- To ease social interactions (53.8%)

----

*Sample survey of 1232 male and female college students and their use of alcohol and other drugs

Drugs and Society Eighth Edition — Chapter 16

Drug Use by College Students

- Most popular substance use and abuse is alcohol (90% of college students)
- College students who frequently binge drink are more likely to smoke cigarettes and use illegal drugs as well
- A clear relationship exists between alcohol use and grade point average (GPA). (The more alcohol consumed the lower the GPA)

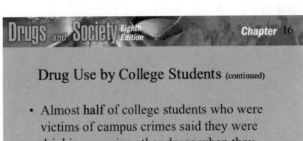

Drug Use by College Students (continued)

- Almost **half** of college students who were victims of campus crimes said they were drinking or using other drugs when they were victimized
- Researchers estimate that alcohol use is implicated in one- to two-thirds of sexual assault and acquaintance or date rape cases among teens and college students

Drug Use by College Students (continued)

- 39% binged on alcohol
- Whites are highest binge drinkers followed by blacks and then Asians
- High percentage of drinkers (approx. 50%) had altercations with law enforcement officials while consuming extraordinary amounts of alcohol

Drug Use by College Students (continued)

- Fill in the blanks regarding recent surveys on lifetime drug patterns of full-time college students.
  A.__% had used alcohol
  B.__% had used cigarettes
  C.__% had used MDMA (Ecstasy)
  D.__% had used marijuana
  Key: A is 83%, B is 41%, C is 9%, and D is 36%.

Notes

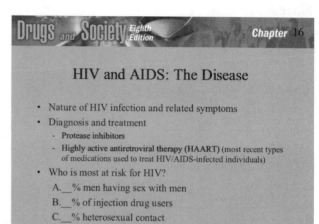

HIV and AIDS: The Disease

- Nature of HIV infection and related symptoms
- Diagnosis and treatment
  - Protease inhibitors
  - Highly active antiretroviral therapy (HAART) (most recent types of medications used to treat HIV/AIDS-infected individuals)
- Who is most at risk for HIV?
  A.__% men having sex with men
  B.__% of injection drug users
  C.__% heterosexual contact
  Key: A is 53%, B is 27%, and C is 13%.

Findings Regarding Age at Diagnosis of HIV and AIDS

- HIV is 5th leading cause of death for all Americans between ages of 25 and 44.
- For black men and women, HIV is the number one cause of death.
- In the U.S., 80% of all people affected with AIDS are male and 20% are female. Worldwide, 73 women are infected for every 100 infected men.
- Florida, Texas, New Jersey, and North Carolina reported the highest number of persons with HIV infection in 1999 (CDC 2000).

Leading Causes for the Spread of HIV/AIDS

- Intravenous drug use – Most important factor for the spread of HIV/AIDS
- Crack – encourages high risk sexual activities

Notes

Drugs and Society Eighth Edition — Chapter 16

Adolescents / Youth and Aids

- Out of 40,000 new cases of HIV infection, 50% of these cases may be among young people under the age of 25.
- Though only 25% of U.S. population, adolescent African-Americans and adolescent Hispanic Americans represent 56% of males with AIDS and 82% of adolescent females with AIDS .

Drugs and Society Eighth Edition — Chapter 16

Adolescents / Youth and Aids (continued)

- The proportion of females with AIDS among U.S. adolescents has more than tripled in the past 10 years — from 14% of the reported cases in 1987 to 46% in 1996.
- For adolescents those most at risk are young gay and bisexual males, particularly young men of color.
- Adolescents who are most vulnerable to HIV infection include homeless or runaways, juvenile offenders, and school dropouts.

Drugs and Society Eighth Edition — Chapter 16

Drug Use in the Entertainment Industry

- Alcohol appeared in 93% of movies, 17% of songs; tobacco appeared in 89% of movies
- Sixty-three percent of rap songs contained reference to substances
- In movies depicting illicit drugs, marijuana appeared most frequently (51%); hallucinogens, heroin and other opiates, and miscellaneous others (each 12%); and crack cocaine (2%)

Notes

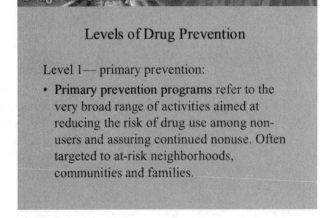

Levels of Drug Prevention

Level 1— primary prevention:

- **Primary prevention programs** refer to the very broad range of activities aimed at reducing the risk of drug use among non-users and assuring continued nonuse. Often targeted to at-risk neighborhoods, communities and families.

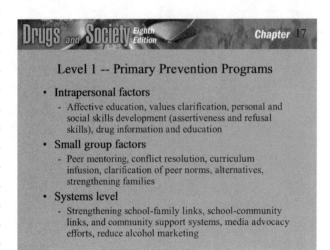

Level 1 -- Primary Prevention Programs

- **Intrapersonal factors**
  - Affective education, values clarification, personal and social skills development (assertiveness and refusal skills), drug information and education
- **Small group factors**
  - Peer mentoring, conflict resolution, curriculum infusion, clarification of peer norms, alternatives, strengthening families
- **Systems level**
  - Strengthening school-family links, school-community links, and community support systems, media advocacy efforts, reduce alcohol marketing

Drugs *and* **Society** *Eighth Edition*   *Chapter* 17

Levels of Drug Prevention

- Level 2 — secondary prevention
- Secondary prevention targets at-risk groups, *early* experimenters and abuse populations in order to stop the progression to drugs of abuse (similar to "early intervention")

Drugs *and* **Society** *Eighth Edition*   *Chapter* 17

Level 2 -- Secondary Drug Prevention Programs

- Assessment strategies: identification of abuse subgroups and individual diagnoses
- Early intervention coupled with sanctions
- Teacher-counselor-parent team approach
- Developing healthy alternative youth culture
- Use of recovering role models

Drugs *and* **Society** *Eighth Edition*   *Chapter* 17

Levels of Drug Prevention

- Level 3 -- tertiary prevention.
- Tertiary prevention is intervention at an advanced state of drug use/abuse. Very similar to drug abuse treatment.

Drugs *and* **Society** *Eighth Edition*   **Chapter** 17

Level 3 -- Tertiary Prevention Programs

- Assessment and diagnosis
- Referral to treatment
- Case management
- Reentry

Drugs *and* **Society** *Eighth Edition*   **Chapter** 17

The Critical Importance of Considering the Type of Audience and Approach

Realize That Audiences Remarkably Differ with Regard to Drug Use:

1. Early experimenters of drugs
2. Non problem drug users—those who abuse drugs on occasion, mostly for recreation purposes
3. Non detected, committed, or secret users—those who abuse drugs and have no interest in stopping
4. Problem users
5. Former users

Drugs *and* **Society** *Eighth Edition*   **Chapter** 17

Comprehensive Prevention Programs for Drug Use and Abuse

Q. What are some of the unique characteristics/examples of the following?

1. Community-Based Prevention?
2. School-Based Drug Prevention?
3. Family-Based Prevention Programs?

Notes

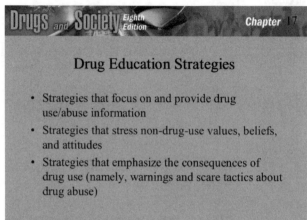

Drug Education Strategies

- Strategies that focus on and provide drug use/abuse information
- Strategies that stress non-drug-use values, beliefs, and attitudes
- Strategies that emphasize the consequences of drug use (namely, warnings and scare tactics about drug abuse)

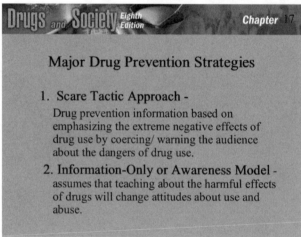

Major Drug Prevention Strategies

1. **Scare Tactic Approach -**
   Drug prevention information based on emphasizing the extreme negative effects of drug use by coercing/ warning the audience about the dangers of drug use.
2. **Information-Only or Awareness Model -**
   assumes that teaching about the harmful effects of drugs will change attitudes about use and abuse.

Major Drug Prevention Strategies (continued)

3. **Attitude change model or affective education model** - assumes people use drugs because of a lack of self-esteem and other personality factors.
4. **Social influences model** – assumes that drug users lack resistance skills. Examples include teaching skills to resist drug use.

Notes

_____

Major Drug Prevention Strategies (continued)

5. Ecological or Person-in-Environment Model – focuses on the causes of drug use resulting largely from the social environment (drug use and abuse problems among the young are social). **Major prevention strategies include:**

1) dissemination of drug information, (2) cognitive and behavioral skills training for youth, parents, and professionals, and mass media, 3) mass media programming, 4) grass roots citizen participation, 5) leadership training, and (6) policy analysis and reformulation

Making Drug Education Programs More Effective

- Practice deliberate planning
- Review the previous history
- Establish links between the messages conveyed and learned and other aspects of students' life experiences
- Effectively promote programs
- Properly allocate resources
- Constantly evaluate effectiveness of program

Examples of Current Large-Scale Drug Prevention Programs

- **Bacchus and Gamma Peer Education Network** – found on college campuses, promotes socializing without alcohol use.
- **D.A.R.E. (Drug Abuse Resistance Education)** – school-based drug education programs by law enforcement officials.
- **Drug Courts** - courts designed to focus on treatment programs and options instead of purely punishing for drug offenders. Criminal justice collaborates and shares power with substance abuse treatment community members in rendering decisions regarding outcome of drug use offenses.

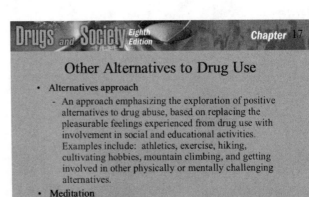

Other Alternatives to Drug Use

- Alternatives approach
  - An approach emphasizing the exploration of positive alternatives to drug abuse, based on replacing the pleasurable feelings experienced from drug use with involvement in social and educational activities. Examples include: athletics, exercise, hiking, cultivating hobbies, mountain climbing, and getting involved in other physically or mentally challenging alternatives.
- Meditation
  - A state of consciousness in which there is a constant level of awareness focusing on one object; for example, getting involved in yoga and/or Zen Buddhism.

A Question for Discussion

- What is your assessment in using the alternatives approach and/or meditation as a method for preventing drug use? Do you think it can be effective for individuals more likely to use and/or abuse drugs? Why or why not?

Chapter 18: Treating Drug Dependence

Notes

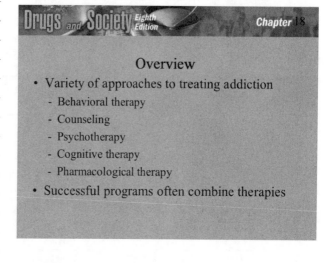

Overview
- Variety of approaches to treating addiction
  - Behavioral therapy
  - Counseling
  - Psychotherapy
  - Cognitive therapy
  - Pharmacological therapy
- Successful programs often combine therapies

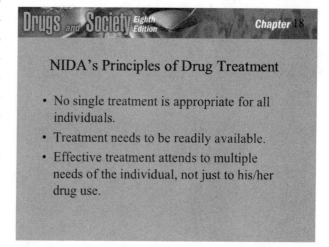

NIDA's Principles of Drug Treatment

- No single treatment is appropriate for all individuals.
- Treatment needs to be readily available.
- Effective treatment attends to multiple needs of the individual, not just to his/her drug use.

Principles of Drug Treatment

- An individual's treatment plan must be assessed continually.
- Remaining in treatment for an adequate period is critical.
- Counseling and other behavioral therapies are critical.

Principles of Drug Treatment

- Medications are important for many patients.
- Addicted or drug-abusing individuals with co-existing mental disorders should have both disorders treated.
- Medical detoxification is only the first step.
- Treatment does not need to be voluntary to be effective.

Principles of Drug Treatment

- Possible drug use during treatment must be monitored continuously.
- Treatment programs should provide assessment for other diseases.
- Recovery can be a long-term process and frequently requires multiple episodes of treatment.

Notes

Drugs and **Society** *Eighth Edition*   Chapter 18

Treatment of Addiction

- Variety of approaches
  - Pharmacological
  - Short- or long-term
  - Individualized or group
  - Many programs combine approaches

Drugs and **Society** *Eighth Edition*   Chapter 18

Historical Approaches

- Alcoholics Anonymous
  - Open and closed meetings

- Rehabilitation facilities
  - "Twelve-stepping"
  - Minnesota Model

Drugs and **Society** *Eighth Edition*   Chapter 18

Other General Strategies

- Medical detoxification
- Outpatient drug-free treatment
- Short-term residential
- Long-term residential
- Criminal justice-involved abusers

Specific Therapeutic Strategies

- Relapse prevention
- The Matrix Model
- Supportive-expressive psychotherapy
- Individualized drug counseling
- Motivational enhancement therapy
- Community reinforcement/vouchers

Examples of Pharmacological Strategies

- Opioid agonist maintenance therapy
- Nicotine replacement therapy
- Antagonist therapy (e.g., naloxone)
- Other examples (e.g., clonidine, disulfiram)

Drug Addiction Treatment Act of 2000

- Subutex and Suboxone
- Drugs can be prescribed in an office setting
- Provides greater patient access to treatment

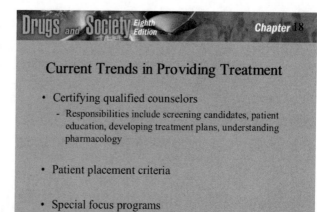